:: *Gardner Family* ::
front row: Sam, Shelby, Sterling, Shelli, Tanner, Zach, Cameron.
second row: Stella, Sara, Sidney, Sean, Seth, Shanna, Nate, Megan, Olivia.
third row: Jon, Ashton, Shalae, Cooper, Jason, Kona, Sage.

dear friends

This is an exciting twentieth-anniversary catalog—we're offering a greater variety of styles, images, and products than we ever have before. There's something that will appeal to everyone, from big and bold images to delicate line art, from traditional to contemporary, from whimsical to tender. What a wonderful way to celebrate this milestone!

This is also the first catalog where my full Shelli's Signature Collection appears. We launched it in our Holiday Mini Catalog, but this is the first complete offering, with several stamp sets and accessories, and even a wheel! I enjoy getting more involved in the creative process of these items.

Be sure to check out our Big Shot® (page 193), along with the full line of die cuts—some exclusive to Stampin' Up!® while others are from Sizzix®'s line of dies. I love what I've been able to create with this exciting tool!

And another thing worth pointing out—all stamp sets are die cut! We thought you'd like that!

One final thing I am thrilled about is all the coordination that I see in this catalog. We have punches that coordinate with sets that coordinate with Designer Series paper that coordinates with ribbon that coordinates with... well, you get the picture. Offering coordinating products makes creating so much easier, faster, and simpler for those of us who are looking to save time yet still create eye-catching works of art.

While these are all terrific ways to celebrate our twentieth anniversary, the biggest reason for celebrating is our relationship with you! Thank you for letting us share our creative ideas and products with you. Here's to the next twenty years!

Shelli

Shelli Gardner
Cofounder and CEO

table of contents

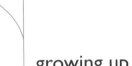

holidays
Share your enthusiasm for your favorite holidays with these sets designed to help you celebrate in style.

hostess opportunity
Don't miss out on these exclusive hostess products. Host a workshop and you can earn them free!

occasions
Observe the special times and momentous occasions in your life such as birthdays, babies, weddings, and more.

growing up
Make your memories last with stamp sets that commemorate every stage of your child's life.

:: featured images ::
You'll find the botanical images shown on these pages in the *Sweet Stems* and *Playful Petals* (page 99) sets.

Receive a discount!

See page 14 to discover
how you can make money
and get a discount on
our products.

all natural

*The images in these sets
capture the inspiring beauty
of nature. Use them to share
your love of the outdoors.*

elements

*Borders, backgrounds,
accents, and labels—our
elements sets have all
you need to put the final
touch on your projects.*

greetings

*Say the perfect thing with our
greetings stamp sets. Stamp
a phrase or create your own
with one of our alphabets.*

accessories

*Indulge your creative
desires with our full line
of accessories including
paper, ink, embellishments,
and much more!*

color families

Stampin' Up! makes choosing color combinations easy! With our four color families, In Color collection, and selection of neutral colors, you're sure to find coordinating colors that you'll love for every project. A wide variety of products—such as card stock, ink pads, ribbon, markers, and brads—are offered in these exclusive Stampin' Up! colors, so you'll coordinate your projects effortlessly. See the charts on pages 153–155 for products available in each color family.

in color
:: page 155 ::

Don't miss our exciting In Color palette of on-trend colors,
available only through June 30. Ask your demonstrator for details.

kiwi kiss	baja breeze	tangerine tango
pink pirouette	pacific point	riding hood red

neutrals
:: page 155 ::

whisper white	very vanilla	sahara sand	sems gray	basic gray	basic brown	basic black

bold brights®
:: *page 154* ::

glorious green	*only orange*	*orchid opulence*
green galore	*real red*	*lovely lilac*
sable green	*pink passion*	*brilliant blue*
yoyo yellow	*pixie pink*	*tempting turquoise*

earth elements®
:: *page 154* ::

chocolate chip	*pumpkin pie*	*summer sun*
close to cocoa	*really rust*	*old olive*
creamy caramel	*ruby red*	*garden green*
more mustard	*cameo coral*	*not quite navy*

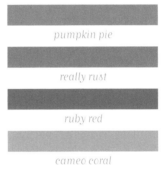

rich regals®
:: *page 155* ::

bordering blue	*taken with teal*	*regal rose*
brocade blue	*handsome hunter*	*rose red*
ballet blue	*always artichoke*	*bravo burgundy*
night of navy	*so saffron*	*elegant eggplant*

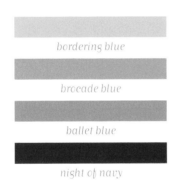

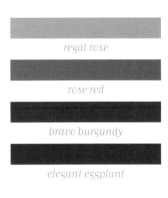

soft subtles®
:: *page 155* ::

perfect plum	*apricot appeal*	*sage shadow*
pale plum	*barely banana*	*bashful blue*
pretty in pink	*certainly celery*	*almost amethyst*
blush blossom	*mellow moss*	*lavender lace*

:: all stamps in this Idea Book & Catalog are shown at actual size unless otherwise noted ::

our stamps

Stampin' Up! offers exclusive coordinating stamp sets you can't find anywhere else. The foam-backed rubber and deeply etched designs on each stamp ensure that your images remain sharp and your projects look exceptional. Some stamp sets are double-mounted, with two stamps sharing one wood block. And all sets now come die cut—so you can assemble them in seconds and start stamping right away!

Don't miss our selection of stamps under $10 (page 208). The options make it easy to start stamping!

Stampin' Up! provides quality products at a terrific value. With hundreds of sets to choose from, you're sure to find the right one for your handcrafted creations.

Our images earned the 2008 Creating Keepsakes Readers' Choice Award for best rubber stamps—for the eighth year in a row!

:: featured image ::
You'll find the stamp image shown above in the Easter Beauty set (page 29).

our products

In addition to our exclusive stamps, we offer many exciting product lines. Three of our newest lines are featured below. Don't miss these stylish and versatile products that will help you create unforgettable projects! See more product lines and our complete line of accessories beginning on page 152.

décor elements

:: you'll find a sampling of our Décor Elements™ on page 192 ::

Personalize your surroundings with our Décor Elements, a variety of exclusive images designed to create a customized, unique space. With our self-adhesive vinyl elements (which are easy to apply and remove), you'll discover how easy and cost effective it can be to do your own decorating! See our complete line in the Décor Elements catalog.

shelli's signature collection

:: marked with a heart ::

Shelli's Signature Collection includes a variety of products that reflect the personal style of Stampin' Up! cofounder Shelli Gardner. To see Shelli's product picks throughout the catalog, look for stamp sets and accessories marked with a heart symbol. Then, try them out to see what you can create!

Products marked with this symbol are part of the exciting new Shelli's Signature Collection.

big shot

:: see our complete offering on pages 195–205 ::

We've teamed up with Sizzix® to offer a multipurpose die-cutting system! With the Sizzix Big Shot Starter Kit and dies from Stampin' Up!, you can create die-cut shapes, envelopes, and tags with ease! Use the Big Shot with our dies—or any dies in the market.

For additional new products, see our Style Watch section on the following six pages, which feature coordinating stamp sets and accessories in stylish new trends!

manhattan

Sophisticated and subtle, our Manhattan collection represents timeless elegance.
This fashionable style combines clean lines, smooth contours, and classic textures. A neutral palette
softened by pale swathes of colors embodies the modern and urban Manhattan Style.

style WATCH

color scheme

| KIWI KISS | BAJA BREEZE | KRAFT | CHOCOLATE CHIP | BASIC GRAY | BASIC BLACK |

coordinating stamp sets

Park Avenue Patterns
114445 **$19.95**
page 107

Central Park
113732 **$15.95**
page 106

Gallery
113776 **$22.95**
page 107

Introducing
114443 **$15.95**
page 143

Fifth Avenue Floral
113734 **$24.95**
page 106

coordinating accessories

Urban Oasis
Designer Series Paper
113978 **$9.95**
page 161

Baja Breeze
1" Double-Stitched Ribbon
111847 **$8.95**
page 178

Fashion District
Rub-Ons
113884 **$10.95**
page 172

Canvas Cuts
Accents & Elements
113979 **$7.95**
page 177

Blooms Again
Die Cuts
112010 **$8.95**
page 181

Manhattan Flower
Décor Elements
$23.95
page 192

Soho
Designer Hardware
114350 **$4.95**
page 175

Taste of Textiles
Specialty Paper
113991 **$9.95**
page 156

Basic Gray
Taffeta Ribbon
109064 **$6.95**
page 179

Beautiful Butterflies
Big Shot Bigz™ Die
114507 **$21.95**
page 196

color scheme

ROSE RED	PUMPKIN PIE	SUMMER SUN	KIWI KISS	CHOCOLATE CHIP	PACIFIC POINT

coordinating stamp sets

Petal Pizzazz
113417 $32.95
page 90

Trendy Trees
113258 $17.95
page 91

Cheep Talk
113204 $26.95
page 90

Really Retro
113754 $14.95
page 132

Good Friend
113740 $28.95
page 91

coordinating accessories

**Flower Assortment
Designer Brads**
112583 $6.95
page 175

**On Board
So Tweet**
113893 $14.95
page 183

**Bright Delights
Rub-Ons**
113887 $11.95
page 172

**Fine Supernova
Stampin' Glitter**
114287 $13.95
page 180

**Sweet
Sticky Cuts**
114301 $8.95
page 180

**Good Morning Sunshine
Designer Series Paper**
113966 $9.95
page 160

**Hooray
Designer Hardware**
114351 $4.95
page 175

**Cherry Blossom
Big Shot Embosslits Die**
114516 $11.95
page 202

**Full Heart
Punch**
113693 $15.95
page 184

**Pig Tails
Ribbon Originals**
114316 $13.95
page 178

retro fresh

The Retro Fresh collection updates a retro style with a fresh twist. Bright, vivid colors and bold patterns bring a playful look to your handcrafted creations. Funky images and patterns featuring flowers and birds help create the distinctive Retro Fresh Style.

style WATCH

sweet bella

The Sweet Bella collection embodies all that is soft and sweet—from its elegant color scheme to its graceful floral images. With these products, you're sure to create chic and stylish keepsakes. Intricate patterns and subtle hues create the unforgettable Sweet Bella Style.

style WATCH

TABLE
3

THANKS

WEDDING DAY
programs

Marcel
AND
Candace

JUNE 14, 2008
DEER VALLEY RESORT
PARK CITY, UTAH

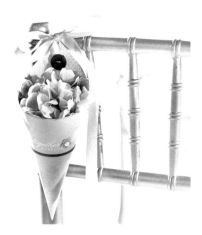

color scheme

| BAJA BREEZE | SO SAFFRON | KIWI KISS | CHOCOLATE CHIP | PINK PIROUETTE | RIDING HOOD RED |

coordinating stamp sets

Dreams du Jour
111624 **$18.95**
page 80

Friends 24-7
113218 **$25.95**
page 81

Ever After
113401 **$22.95**
page 83

Spring Song
115074 **$15.95**
page 82

Flower Fancy
111578 **$36.95**
page 80

coordinating accessories

**Whisper White
Organza Ribbon**
114319 **$5.95**
page 179

**Eyelet Border
Punch**
113692 **$15.95**
page 184

**Button Bouquet
Designer Buttons**
112092 **$7.95**
page 176

**Sweet Nothings
Simply Scrappin'**
113925 **$19.95**
page 164

**Dress Up
Ribbon Originals**
114317 **$12.95**
page 178

**Fleurettes
Accents & Elements**
114019 **$9.95**
page 177

**Parisian Breeze
Specialty
Designer Series Paper**
113993 **$11.95**
page 158

**Chateau Bella
Rub-Ons**
111416 **$10.95**
page 172

**Pretties
Kit**
109114 **$29.95**
page 175

**Bella Birds
Designer Series Paper**
113981 **$9.95**
page 160

start with Stampin' Up!

Share your love for creativity by starting your own business as a Stampin' Up!
demonstrator. You can make money, set your own hours, and get a discount on our products!
Talk to your demonstrator to learn more, then buy a Starter Kit to get started today!

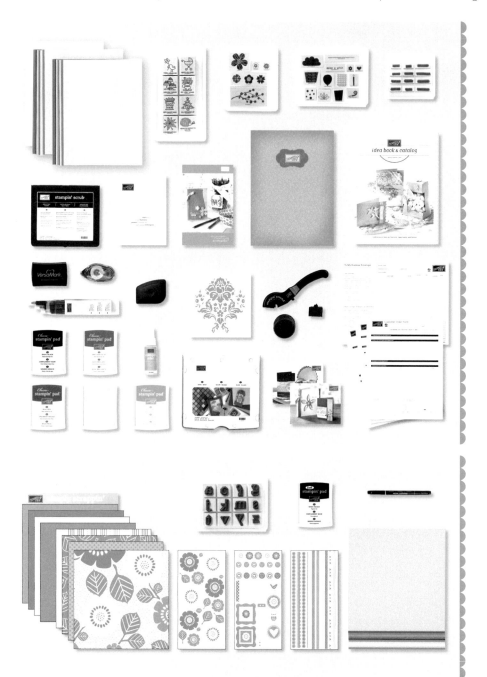

starter kit $199
:: *valued at more than $555* ::

Eastern Blooms Stamp Set
Fun & Fast Notes Stamp Set
Big Bold Birthday Stamp Set
Fundamental Phrases Stamp Set *(double-mounted)*
Fast Flowers Wheel
Stampin' Around Self-Inking Handle
Pixie Pink Ink Cartridge
Stampin' Pastels
Bold Brights Assorted 8.5" × 11" Card Stock *(2)*
Kraft Parisian Damask Décor Elements *(large)*
Décor Elements applicator tool
Stampin' Scrub
Stampin' Mist
VersaMark Pad
Blender Pens
Whisper White Card Stock
SNAIL Adhesive
Basic Black Classic Stampin' Pad
Real Red Classic Stampin' Pad
Brilliant Blue Classic Stampin' Pad
Green Galore Classic Stampin' Pad
Pixie Pink Classic Stampin' Pad
Business Forms and Tools

stampin' memories
add-on $50
:: *valued at more than $80* ::

Bold Brights Assorted 12" × 12" Card Stock
Schoolbook Serif Alphabet *(double-mounted)*
Petal Party Simply Scrappin'
Whisper White Craft Stampin' Pad
Basic Black Stampin' Write Journaler

www.stampinup.com 1-800-STAMP UP

hostess

Stampin' Up! hostesses enjoy a fun get-together with family and friends to share the fun of creativity. At this gathering, your demonstrator will present creative projects, and you'll have the opportunity to earn free products!

earn free products!

When you host a qualifying workshop, you'll earn free products, plus your demonstrator will give you a free *Spring-Summer 2009 Idea Book & Catalog*. Schedule a workshop and start earning!

With net workshop sales of only $150, you can select one of our Level 1 hostess sets.

level 1
:: pages 17–18 ::

Select from our Level 2 hostess sets with net workshop sales of $500 or more.

level 2
:: pages 19–20 ::

Once your net workshop sales reach $500, you can choose from our selection of Level 3 sets.

level 3
:: pages 21–25 ::

:: *featured images* ::
You'll find the stamp images shown on this page in *God's Beauty* (page 17), *A Little Somethin'* (page 20), and *Goody-Goody Gumdrops* (page 22) sets.

net workshop total	hostess sets level 1	level 2	level 3	hostess awards free merchandise totaling up to:
$150.00–$199.99	choose 1	—	—	$15.00
$200.00–$249.99	choose 1	—	—	$20.00
$250.00–$299.99	choose 1	—	—	$25.00
$300.00–$349.99	choose 1	or choose 1	—	$35.00
$350.00–$399.99	choose 1	or choose 1	—	$40.00
$400.00–$449.99	choose 2	—	—	$45.00
	or choose 1	choose 1	—	
$450.00–$499.99	choose 2	—	—	$50.00
	or choose 1	choose 1	—	
$500.00–$549.99	choose 3	—	—	$60.00
	or choose 2	choose 1	—	
	or choose 1	—	choose 1	
$550.00–$599.99	choose 3	—	—	$65.00
	or choose 2	choose 1	—	
	or choose 1	—	choose 1	
$600.00–$649.99	choose 2	choose 1	—	$75.00
	or choose 1	choose 2	—	
	or —	choose 1	choose 1	
	or choose 3	—	—	
	or choose 1	—	choose 1	
$650.00–$699.99	choose 2	choose 1	—	$85.00
	or choose 1	choose 2	—	
	or —	choose 1	choose 1	
	or choose 3	—	—	
	or choose 1	—	choose 1	
$700.00–$749.99	choose 2	—	choose 1	$95.00
	or choose 1	choose 1	choose 1	
	or —	—	choose 2	
	or choose 3	—	—	
	or choose 2	choose 1	—	
	or choose 1	choose 2	—	
$750.00+	choose 2	—	choose 1	$100 plus 15% of amount over $750.00
	or choose 1	choose 1	choose 1	
	or —	—	choose 2	
	or choose 3	—	—	
	or choose 2	choose 1	—	
	or choose 1	choose 2	—	

:: *shipping & handling is not charged on hostess benefits* ::

Beauty is God's handwriting.
~ Ralph Waldo Emerson

ESP 114633   La belleza de Dios

God's Beauty | set of
(level 1) 113222 | 4

ESP 114629   Querida amiga

dear friend

Dear Friend | set of
(level 1) 113413 | 4

i loaf you

feeling sick?
milk it.

donut be sad

pop on by

Comfort Food | set of
(level 1) 113210 | 4

donut be sad

SHOWN IN REGAL ROSE

Patterns Pack Designer Series Paper II

Hostesses can choose this 6" × 6" pad of our Patterns Designer Series paper. This pack features an assortment of 5 colors never before offered in the Patterns line. 60 sheets: 2 ea. of 6 double-sided designs in each color.

	114325	Patterns Pack II	level 1
		Regal Rose, Apricot Appeal, Brocade Blue, Basic Gray, Garden Green	

hello little baby
{welcome home!}

a note for you

because nice matters

to wonderful you
from thankful me

heart to heart,
hand in hand

celebrate one cupcake
at a time!

take care of yourself

impressed, amazed, inspired
{by you}

set of **8** | **Sweet Little Sentiments**
113690 *(level 1)*

(ESP) 114637 Sentimientos de dulzura

set of **8** | **Darling Dots**
113708 *(level 1)*

(ESP) 114627 Puntos primorosos

Itty Bitty Buds
(level 2) 113720 | set of 14

Kind words
can be
short and *easy*
to speak, but their
echoes are truly
endless.
~Mother Teresa

1-3/4" Circle Punch
112004 $15.95
page 184

Full Heart Punch
113693 $15.95
page 184

set of
6 | **A Little Somethin'**
113415 *(level 2)*

set of
4 | **Rustic Rooster**
113274 *(level 2)*

dwell in possibilities

This was the first summer we took Lizzie up to Grandma Lucy's cabin in Colorado.
She loved all the wildflowers and wanted to stop every few steps to pick another "pretty one."
Every now and then, her flower picking was interrupted by her favorite games
of peek-a-boo and bubble blowing.

SPRING
happiness

dream a little

ESP 114631 Sueña un poco

Dream a Little
(level 3) 113435 | set of 8

Create scalloped edges by using a circle punch (page 184). Just punch out several circles of card stock and adhere them as shown on the Thoughts of You card.

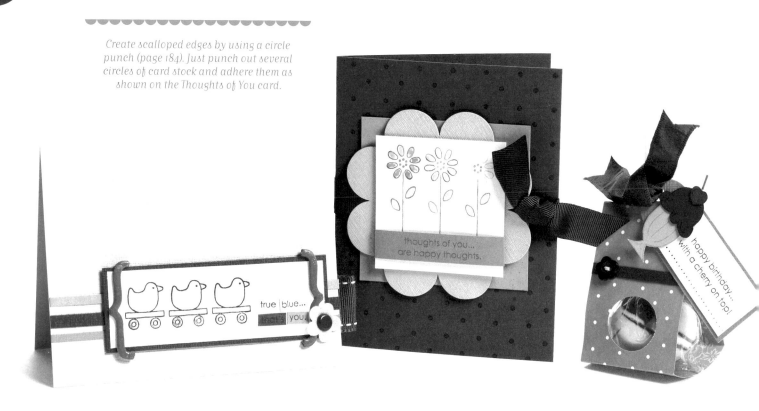

goody-goody gumdrops!

so loved

my cherry-amour

thanks, i owe you one... maybe two!

true blue... that's you.

hello there

you're so sweet

happy birthday... with a cherry on top!

so happy for you... congratulations!

thoughts of you... are happy thoughts.

set of **Goody-Goody Gumdrops**
19 113730 *(level 3)*

ESP 114635 Dulces expresiones

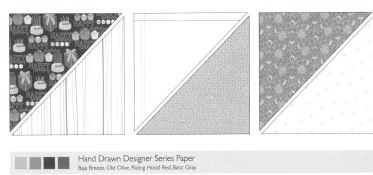

Hand Drawn Designer Series Paper
Baja Breeze, Old Olive, Riding Hood Red, Basic Gray

IT'S A LOOP THING STAMP ARTWORK (SET OF 4)

Hand Drawn Bundle

This level 3 hostess bundle includes 2 sheets of Loop to Loop Rub-Ons (1 ea. Chocolate Chip and Whisper White), 9 sheets of 12" x 12" Designer Series double-sided paper (3 ea. in 3 designs), and the It's a Loop Thing stamp set. These multipurpose images add a fun vibrance to your projects.

| 115535 | Hand Drawn Bundle | level 3 |

Loop to Loop Rub-Ons
Whisper White, Chocolate Chip

step 1
Ink the background stamp with the VersaMark ink pad (page 190).

step 2
Stamp the image.

step 3
Dab a sponge dauber (page 190) on one of our Stampin' Pastels' (page 152).

step 4
Use the Stampin' Pastels eraser to remove the excess chalk from around the image.

poppin' pastels

This technique offers the best of both worlds—stamped images combined with our vibrant pastels. For best results, use bold images such as our Two-Step Stampin' sets. Ask your demonstrator for more tips about and techniques that use our Stampin' Pastels.

:: featured image ::
You'll find the stamp image shown above in the All Holidays set (page 52).

Use the A Happy Heart set with the coordinating Love Sparkles Simply Scrappin' (page 163). You'll love the additional variety of using these products together.

wishing
you a
happy
heart

{FEB.
14}

i♥u

happy valentine's day

set of 6 | **A Happy Heart**
111758 $22.95

HAPPY ♡♡
VALENTINE'S
♡ ♡ ♡ DAY

To someone with a
very big heart!

thank
you

HAPPY HEART DAY

to an unforgettable friend

set of 7 | **Happy Heart Day**
114978 $23.95

**Heart to Heart
Punch**
113694 **$15.95**
page 184

**Candy Lane
Designer Series Paper**
113980 **$9.95**
page 159

friend to friend

**5-Point 3D Star
Big Shot Bigz Die**
113473 **$19.95**
page 196

you much

ESP 114022 Te quiero mucho

Love You Much | *set of* 6
113756 **$25.95**

love love love

You & Moi | *set of* 6
111716 **$12.95**

HAPPY ST. PATRICK'S DAY

march 08

Lucky me!
I've got you

Pinch Proof
set of 6 | 115044 **$22.95**

LUCKY ME PINCH ME
if you're irish you're lucky enough
DANCE a jig
LEPRECHAUN GOLD green
HAPPY ST. PATTY'S DAY

Pinch Me
111259 **$8.50** (jumbo)

Circle Designer Brads
112571 **$5.95**
page 175

Pink Pirouette 1-1/4" Grosgrain Ribbon
111363 **$7.95**
page 179

Certainly Celery Patterns Designer Series Paper
112154 **$9.95**
page 159

The "Happy Easter" and "You crack me up" greetings share one wood block. Simply ink and stamp the image you need.

happy easter

you crack me up

A Good Egg | *set of*
114974 **$23.95** | 7

May the miracle of Easter
bring you renewed faith, hope, and happiness.

May the miracle of Easter
bring you renewed faith, hope, and happiness

ESP 114024   Bella Pascua

Easter Beauty | *set of*
113750 **$24.95** | 8

Scallop Edge Punch
112091 **$15.95**
page 184

Scallop Notes II
111336 **$11.95**
page 157

Clips Assortment
112580 **$6.95**
page 176

Thinking of You
on
FATHER'S DAY

set of **Thoughts of Father**
3 | 115094 **$15.95**

set of **Blooming with Love**
8 | 114936 **$24.95**

 Blooms & Bulbs
| 111253 **$6.50**

happy
4th!

Independence Day | *set of* 7
114992 $23.95

What LOVE is
to the HEART,
LIBERTY is to
the SOUL.

The Free & the Brave | *set of* 4
114962 $21.95

31

Give your projects subtle elegance by using tone-on-tone embellishments such as the word "Friend" on the card below.

MY *dear* KIND & *wonderful* FRIEND

HAPPY **mother's** DAY

for you

{ thank you }

HAPPY FATHER'S DAY

HAPPY HALLOWEEN

Peace Love Joy

Easter Wishes

Mr. & Mrs.

hugs & kisses

Merry CHRISTMAS

h a p p y   b i r t h d a y

set of 12 | **All Holidays**
114916 **$34.95**

 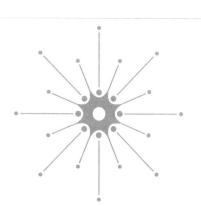 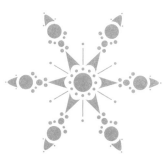  

set of 6 | **Snow Burst**
110386 **$19.95**

Button Bouquet
112092 **$7.95**
page 176

Beautiful Butterflies Big Shot Bigz Die
114507 **$21.95**
page 196

So Saffron 1/2" Striped Grosgrain Ribbon
113699 **$7.95**
page 178

xoxoxo

dear
dad

my
mom

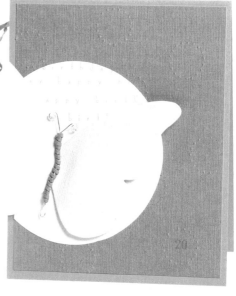

thank
you

Holiday Blitz | set of
114982 **$38.95** | 28

HAPPY
Thanksgiving

Happy Valentine's Day

from the heart

HAPPY
NEW YEAR

Merry
Christmas

sweet little one

Holidays & Wishes | set of
114984 **$18.95** | 6

**Aluminum White Circle
Metal Edge Tags**
103374 **$4.25**
page 176

**Bashful Blue Patterns
Designer Series Paper**
112151 **$9.95**
page 159

Crimper
101618 **$19.95**
page 189

33

Wishing you the joy and wonder
of the first Christmas.

Christ is Born

Let the heavens rejoice and the earth be glad.
~ Psalm 96:11

set of 3 | **Christ Is Born**
111612 **$20.95**

set of 6 | **Spotlight on Christmas**
111694 **$22.95**

1-1/4" Square Punch
104400 **$15.95**
page 184

Top Note Big Shot Bigz Die
113463 **$21.95**
page 196

Riding Hood Red 5/8" Striped Grosgrain Ribbon
111374 **$9.95**
page 178

have a holly, ¡olly Christmas!

joy

Create a scalloped edge with ease using our easy-to-align, exclusive Scallop Edge punch (page 184) that ensures even placement no matter how long the border.

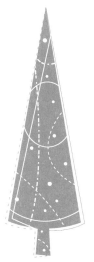

to:

from:

ESP 112889 Una alegre y feliz Navidad

A Holly, Jolly Christmas *set of* **8**
111558 **$26.95**

warm wishes

TO:

FROM:

HOLIDAY CHEER

ESP 112921 Felices fiestas

Heritage Holiday *set of* **7**
111646 **$20.95**

On Board Essentials
112085 **$12.95**
page 182

Scallop Edge Punch
112091 **$15.95**
page 184

Mini Library Clips
109857 **$12.95**
page 176

step 1
Dab a sponge dauber (page 190) on one of our Craft Stampin' Pads (pages 153–155).

step 2
Ink the chipboard with the desired color.

step 3
Use our heat tool (page 186) to set the ink.

coloring chipboard with craft ink

Create chipboard pieces in any of our exclusive colors by coloring them with our Craft Stampin' Pads. Just choose an On Board assortment (pages 182–183) and ink color for your project, then follow these easy steps to create the perfect embellishment. Ask your demonstrator to show you other embellishment ideas.

:: *featured image* ::
You'll find the stamp image shown above in the Sip by Sip set (page 51).

occasions

Dear _____,

Thank you for the

_____.

I like it a lot!

Sincerely,

_____

Use the Simple Birthday Thanks stamp to create thank-you notes. For additional versatility, color the stamp with a marker to eliminate any part of the image, such as the sprinkles on the frosting or the text on the cupcake.

set of 1 | **Simple Birthday Thanks**
111546 **$17.95**

make a wish!

happy birthday to you

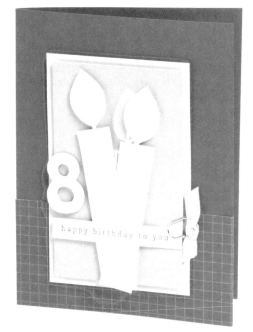

Our Clips Assortment offers fun ways to add embellishments to your projects.

set of 7 | **Big Birthday Candle**
114924 **$24.95**

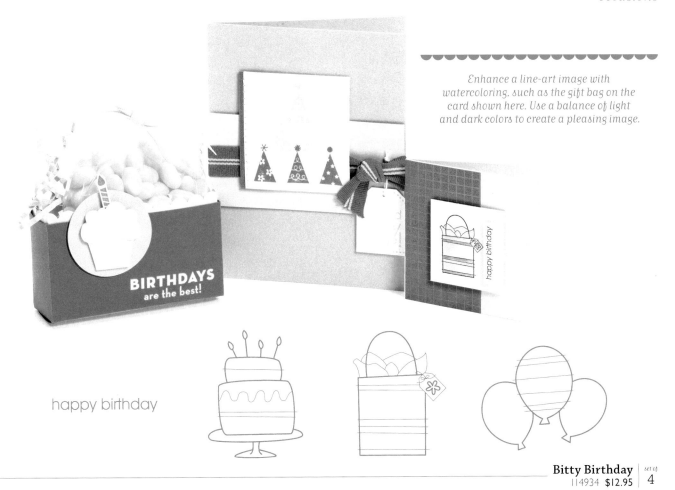

Enhance a line-art image with watercoloring, such as the gift bag on the card shown here. Use a balance of light and dark colors to create a pleasing image.

happy birthday

Bitty Birthday | set of 4
114934 **$12.95**

you take the cake!

party hearty!

C E L E B R A T E Y O U

b is for birthday

...and many more!

Party Hearty | set of 9
111532 **$26.95**

*tiMe*to*cElebRaTe!

Celebration
112477 **$6.50**

Big Bold Cupcakes
Big Shot Sizzlits® 4-Pack Dies
114509 **$21.95**
page 201

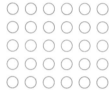

Pacific Point
Corduroy Buttons
114341 **$9.95**
page 176

Neutrals Jumbo
5/16" Brads
112534 **$7.95**
page 174

happybirthday!happybirthday!happybirthday!

make a wish

 set of **13** | **Big Bold Birthday**
114926 **$28.95**

ESP 112895 Cumpleaños genial y divertido

happybirthday!happybirthday!happybirthday!happybirthday!
birthday!happybirthday!happybirthday!happybirthday!happy
thday!happybirthday!happybirthday!happybirthday!happybir
day!happybirthday!happybirthday!happybirthday!happybirth
happybirthday!happybirthday!happybirthday!happybirthday!
thday!happybirthday!happybirthday!happybirthday!happybir
day!happybirthday!happybirthday!happybirthday!happybirth
pybirthday!happybirthday!happybirthday!happybirthday!hap
birthday!happybirthday!happybirthday!happybirthday!happy

 Happy, Happy Birthday
111257 **$8.50** *(jumbo)*

Frame any small square image with our Scallop Square punch (page 184). This simple technique makes the stamped image stand out.

birthday greetings

Time to Party | set of 4
111702 $16.95

happy birthday to you

hope your day is the sweetest ever!

Crazy for Cupcakes | set of 6
111618 $23.95

Cupcakes
113121 $6.50

41

jacob

i'm
pulling
for you.

you float my boat!

i'm
pulling
for you.

friend·ship

you float my boat!

set of **7** | **Boatloads of Love**
114938 **$23.95**

Time for a Tree
104524 **$6.50**

**3/4" Circle
Punch**
107217 **$10.95**
page 184

**Certainly Celery Patterns
Designer Series Paper**
112154 **$9.95**
page 159

**Rose Red
1/4" Grosgrain Ribbon**
111366 **$4.95**
page 179

wishing you
loads of
holiday cheer!

merry
christmas!

moved

thought you could
use a little
pickup!

Loads
of
Love!

thought you
could use
a little
pickup!

 Loads of Love | set of
115022 **$23.95** | **7**

happy
harvest

driving by
with a
birthday
"Hi"!

eggstra
special
easter
wishes!

just
moved!

friends
for the
long haul

Loads of Love Accessories | set of
115024 **$20.95** | **12**

Tailgating
105519 **$6.50**

Jet Black
StāzOn® Ink Pad
101406 **$7.95**
page 190

Aqua Painter®
103954 **$16.95**
page 190

Silver Brads
104336 **$6.95**
page 174

43

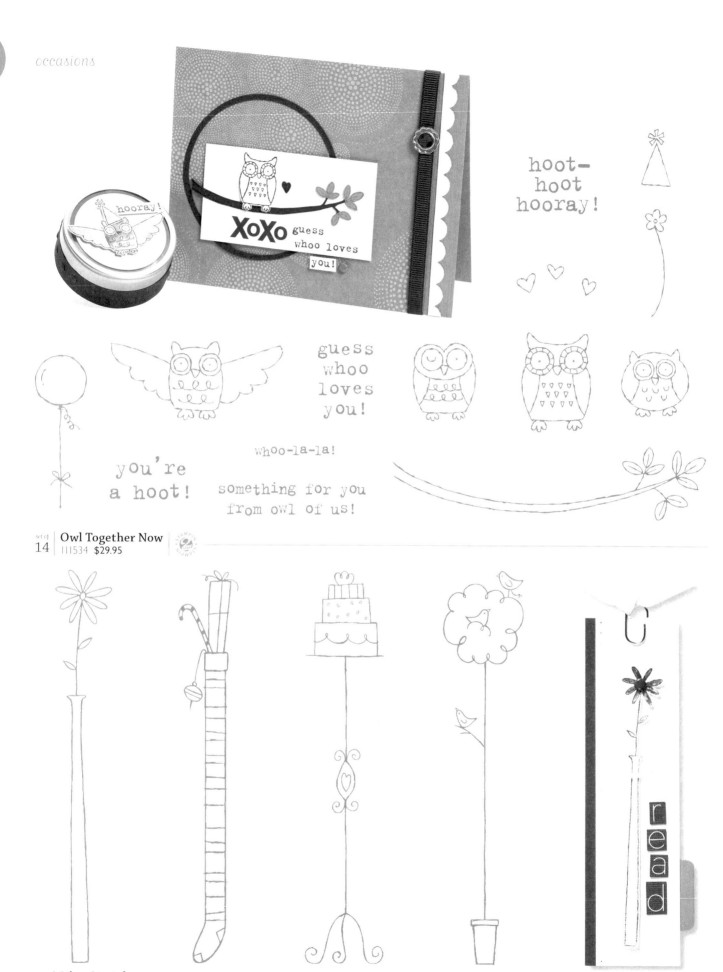

hoot-
hoot
hooray!

hooray!

XoXo guess
whoo loves
you!

guess
whoo
loves
you!

whoo-la-la!

you're
a hoot!

something for you
from owl of us!

set of
14 | **Owl Together Now**
111534 $29.95

read

set of
4 | **It's a Stretch**
111586 $23.95

**Bashful Blue
1" Double-Stitched
Grosgrain Ribbon**
111848 **$8.95**
page 178

Aqua Painter
103954 **$16.95**
page 190

**Spiral
Punch**
108341 **$10.95**
page 184

	Voilà	*set of*
115102	**$25.95**	6

Voilà to Go	*set of*
115104 **$17.95**	6

Create a mini scrapbook with our On Board Book Basics. It's a fun gift that can be decorated for any occasion.

BRAVO ☆ cheers
you're on your way you did it
YOU'RE A STAR
congrats
aim for
GOOD way to go the stars ★
LUCK GOOD JOB big applause
GREAT ACCOMPLISHMENT
SUCCESS LOOKS
GOOD ON YOU
you're on your way
well done ★ ★
kudos Best
YOU'VE COME FAR
celebrate ★ Wishes ★ ★ ★
★ you deserve a
pat on the back

CONGRATULATIONS
congratulations
CONGRATULATIONS

It is not in the **stars** to hold our **destiny** but in **ourselves**.
· WILLIAM SHAKESPEARE ·

grȧd

Great Grads
set of 5 | 114976 $24.95

let a SmiLe be your umbrella.

whole laTTe love

hǎppiNeSs
is never stopping
to think if you are.

Font of You
set of 6 | 113405 $24.95

**To the Nines
Specialty
Designer Series Paper**
114038 $11.95
page 158

**Chocolate Chip
Corduroy Buttons**
114339 $9.95
page 176

thanks for helping me
out of a tight spot.

you hit the nail on the head!

he who has the most tools wins.

love beyond measure

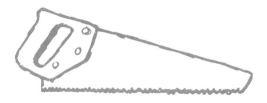

you came, you sawed, you fixed.
thanks for all you do.

Totally Tool | *set of*
113256 $25.95 | 5

You're a blast!

Love you a latte!

Hip-hippo-ray!

Happy bird-day!

Get whale soon!

Thank ewe!

I stink you're sweet!

Purrrfect!

Pun Fun
set of 8 | 115054 **$32.95**

See You Around
109687 **$8.50** *(jumbo)*

Embellish a scalloped border by using a 1/16" Circle punch (page 184) to create a small hole on each scallop. This adds a fun, decorative touch to your projects.

you got a promotion!

you're getting married!

you're under the weather.

it's time to celebrate!

it's your birthday!

about your good news!

a little birdie told me...

you're the best!

A Little Birdie Told Me
115016   **$26.95** | set of 12

Animal Crackers | set of 5
113395   **$19.95**

49

Make your focal point unique by backing it with a frayed piece of Twill Tape (page 179), as shown on the Thanks card.

if the Halo fits...

thanks for being such an angel.

angels can fly because they take themselves lightly.

good friends are like angels— you don't have to see them to know they are there.

| wrap 7 | **If the Halo Fits** 114988 $23.95 |

Perfect Fit
111251 $6.50

thanks a latte!

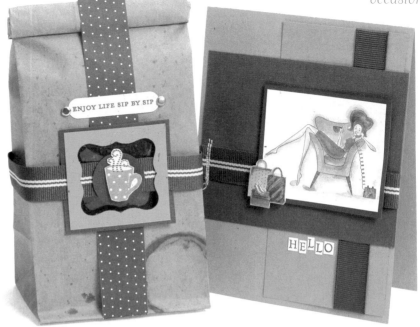

ENJOY LIFE SIP BY SIP

HELLO

Chocolate, coffee, men—
some things are better rich.

ENJOY LIFE SIP BY SIP, NOT GULP BY GULP.

Sip by Sip | *set of* 6
113403 **$23.95**

*A girl should be two things:
classy and fabulous.
— Coco Chanel*

*Women are meant to be
loved, not to be understood.
— Oscar Wilde*

like you

Classy & Fabulous | *set of* 6
113226 **$18.95**

Fashion Forward
113836 **$6.50**

**Riding Hood Red
5/8" Striped
Grosgrain Ribbon**
111374 **$9.95**
page 178

**Bella Rose
Designer Series Paper**
112041 **$9.95**
page 159

**Word Window
Punch**
105090 **$15.95**
page 184

Erin & Levi July 30, 2008

heart

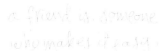

a friend is someone who makes it easy

Simply said from the heart... thank you

Scatter Sunshine
107213 **$8.50** (jumbo)

Kindness
106750 **$8.50** (jumbo)

Change of a dress.

Cinderella is proof that a new pair of shoes can change your life!

I didn't forget your birthday. I'm just fashionably late!

Give a girl the correct footwear and she can conquer the world!

~ Bette Midler

Change of a dress.

Cinderella is proof that a new pair of shoes can change your life!

I didn't forget your birthday. I'm just fashionably late!

Whether you're a good witch or a bad witch, it's all about the shoes!

Humor in High Heels | set ct
111652 **$26.95** | 10

May your sorrows be patched and your joys quilted.

May your bobbin always be full.

In the crazy quilt of life... I'm glad you're in my block of friends.

may your sorrows be patched and your joys quilted.

When life throws you scraps, make a quilt!

Quilt Quips | set ct
113240 **$22.95** | 8

53

HAPPY BIRTHDAY WISHES

TOGETHER FOREVER

GET WELL WISHES

THANKS...I NEEDED THAT

THANKS FOR SHARING YOU WITH ME

CONGRATULATIONS

HAPPY NEW BABY

ALL SPRUCED UP

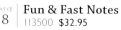

Fun & Fast Notes
8 | 113500 **$32.95**

ESP 112915 Notas rápidas y divertidas

Fast Flowers
109679 **$6.50**

Earth Elements Brads
106955 **$8.95**
page 174

Old Olive 1/2" Striped Grosgrain Ribbon
113883 **$7.95**
page 178

On Board Essentials
112085 **$12.95**
page 182

Make the most of the Best Wishes & More set by using it with the coordinating Petal Party Simply Scrappin' (page 162).

thank you

couldn't do without you.

laughter joy happiness bliss delight

Wishing you all this...
and more!

ready, set, snow!

Best Wishes & More | set of
111602 **$26.95** | 9

friends

birthday wishes

get well soon

thank you

Garden Greetings | set of
113716 **$21.95** | 8

**Aluminum White Circle
Metal Edge Tags**
103374 **$4.25**
page 176

**Old Olive Patterns
Designer Series Paper**
112160 **$9.95**
page 159

1/2" Library Clips
112581 **$6.95**
page 176

55

**Circle Fire
Rhinestone Brads**
109110 $10.95
page 174

**Riding Hood Red
Taffeta Ribbon**
111365 $6.95
page 179

**Filigree
Designer Brads**
112577 $5.95
page 175

God is love.

Peace be unto you.

Fishers of men

Combine your
hearts as one.

Jesus wants me
for a sunbeam

Wise men
seek him still

God's little lamb

God keeps
his promises

set of **God Is Love**
8 | 114970 $23.95

Love
109692 $6.50

just buzzin' by to say...

have a honey of a day!

Just Buzzin' By | set of
113228 $27.95 | 8

you're
SWEET

A kind word is like a spring day.

♡ | **A Kind Word** | set of
113194 $21.95 | 4

Sharing in your Sorrow

Thinking of You...
Please know that I care.

Wishing you a quick and complete recovery.

GET WELL SOON

Sending thoughts of love and praying for the Lord to sustain you with bright and restful days.

Praying for You...

Praying for friends to comfort you, faith to uphold you, and loving memories to heal your heart.

Thoughts & Prayers
set of 8 | 113252 **$25.95** *(double-mounted)*

WITH HEARTFELT
Sympathy

Your loved one will always be as close as a memory, and the God of all comfort as close as a prayer.

Earth has no sorrow that heaven cannot heal.

—Thomas Moore

Close As a Memory
set of 4 | 114946 **$20.95**

Watercolor Joy
105516 **$6.50**

God is,
and all
is well.
~John Whittier

Each day of life is a
precious gift from God.
~Charles H. Spurgeon

God is our refuge
and strength,
therefore we will
not fear.
Psalm 46:1, 2

God is not too
great
to be concerned
about our
smallest wishes.

In those times
I can't seem to
find God, I rest
in the assurance

He knows how to
find me.
~Neva Coyle

Refuge and Strength
115056 $23.95 | set ct 7

so sorry
to hear of
your loss

get well
soon

thinking
of you

thoughts
and prayers
are with you

heartfelt
wishes

Always in My Thoughts
111562 $17.95 | set ct 6

Heather & Trevor got engaged! June 2008

to have and to hold

a promise made

To Have and to Hold
8 | 115098 **$26.95**

Together Forever
6 | 115100 **$22.95**

Forever Flowers
| 111252 **$6.50**

Create an elegant favor box like the one below to commemorate a wedding or any special occasion.

CONGRATULATIONS

FOR THE BRIDE

YOU'RE INVITED

ESP 114028 Para la novia

For the Bride | set of
113216 **$19.95** | 5

May God bless you...

on your *Special* day

on your *Wedding* day

as you start your *Married Life*

on your *First Communion*

on your *Baptism* day

ESP 114026 Benediciones especiales

Special Blessing | set of
(double-mounted) 113411 **$19.95** | 8

It's a housewarming party!

Cheers to you!

welcome

sad to see you go

We've moved our doorstep.
Our new address is...

It's a housewarming party!

Welcome Home
set of 5 | 113433 **$20.95**

CHeeRS to you!

Cheers to You
set of 6 | 114944 **$17.95**

Cheers
113122 **$6.50**

Clear Stampin' Emboss Powder
109130 **$4.75**
page 186

Button Latte
114333 **$7.95**
page 176

Fashion District Rub-Ons
113884 **$10.95**
page 172

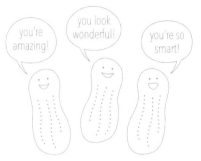

complimentary peanuts

Use our ribbon (pages 178–179) to accent your projects with a touch of color. We offer a variety of styles and colors, so you're sure to find the right one for your creation.

i'm really lucky to have a friend like you...

...since i tend to scare normal people away.
GLAD WE'RE FRIENDS!

a candle for every year might
not be such a good idea...

happy birthday!

Everyone has a
photographic memory...

some just don't have film.

That's Funny | set of
113250 **$23.95** | 4

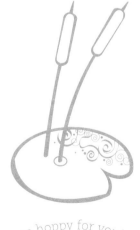

time's fun when
you're having flies.

just hoppin'
all is well!

so hoppy for you!

Hoppy for You | set of
113270 **$23.95** | 9

**Chocolate Chip
1/4" Grosgrain Ribbon**
111367 **$4.95**
page 179

**Urban Garden
Designer Series Paper**
112042 **$9.95**
page 159

**Vintage
Brads**
109109 **$8.95**
page 174

step 1
Use a 1/2" Circle punch to punch out a small circle.

step 2
Cut out a stamped heart with the Heart to Heart punch (page 184).

step 3
Adhere the heart to the brad base.

step 4
Place the adhesive acrylic bubble on the heart.

build-a-brad

If you've ever wanted a custom-made brad for your project, look no further. The Build-A-Brad (page 174) makes it easy to create what you need. Use our stamps, patterned paper, punches, and more to design a unique embellishment to fit any project. Your demonstrator can show you how to use these and other Stampin' Up! products.

:: featured image ::
You'll find the stamp image shown above in the Perfect Princess set (page 71).

growing up

it's a boy!

it's a girl!

little cutie

welcome, little one

so happy for you!

rock-a-bye baby

set of
12 | **Nursery Necessities**
113506 **$31.95**

Nursery Letters
111258 **$8.50** *(jumbo)*

Classic Stars
111254 **$8.50** *(jumbo)*

Pretty in Pink
1/4" Grosgrain Ribbon
109032 **$4.95**
page 179

Clear Buttons
105447 **$4.95**
page 176

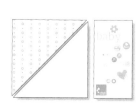
Rock-a-Bye Girl
Simply Scrappin'
112165 **$19.95**
page 165

welcome little one

Small images like those in the Cute & Cuddly set are excellent for making tags. Just stamp the image and punch or cut it out. Layer more than one piece for a dimensional effect.

I'm kind of a
BIG
D·E·A·L

Baby Shower

date ....

time ....

place ....

ESP 114030 Tierno y Cariñoso

♡ **Cute & Cuddly**
113682 **$26.95** | *set of* 6

Zoofari
115116 **$22.95** | *set of* 6

Valet Ribbon Originals
114318 **$12.95**
page 178

Certainly Celery Patterns Designer Series Paper
112154 **$9.95**
page 159

Scallop Square Punch
112081 **$15.95**
page 184

just for you

YOU ROCK!

thanks a bunch!

just for you

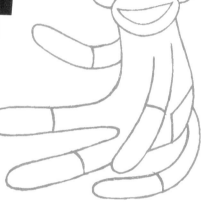

set of
10 | **Sock Monkey**
111550 $26.95

thanks a bunch!

set of
8 | **Sock Monkey Accessories**
111552 $21.95

**Dazzling Diamonds
Stampin' Glitter**
102023 $4.50
page 180

**Riding Hood Red
Taffeta Ribbon**
111365 $6.95
page 179

**1" Circle
Punch**
109046 $10.95
page 184

Use our Circle Scissor® Plus (page 188) to create circles with ease. They are perfect for cropping photos, creating embellishments, and more!

Des and Jessica · 2008

the girlz

YOU ROCK!

Just Jawing | *set of* 6
111660 **$25.95**

Scary Skulls
113119 **$6.50**

Button Bouquet
112092 **$7.95**
page 176

Rockabilly Specialty Designer Series Paper
114039 **$11.95**
page 158

Regal Rose 5/8" Grosgrain Ribbon
109056 **$7.95**
page 179

life's a breeze

set of
13 | **Life's a Breeze**
113504 $31.95

Something Fishy
111260 $8.50 *(jumbo)*

Crimper
101618 $19.95
page 189

Bashful Blue
1/4" Grosgrain Ribbon
109029 $4.95
page 179

Soft Subtles
Brads
106954 $8.95
page 174

...and they lived

happily ever after...   ONCE UPON A TIME...

FAIRY TALES   the end

DO COME TRUE...

Once Upon a Time | set of
113746 **$19.95** | 4

Perfect Princess | set of
115040 **$23.95** | 7

Perfectly Pretty
109682 **$6.50**

**So Saffron Patterns
Designer Series Paper**
112152 **$9.95**
page 159

Pretties Kit
109114 **$29.95**
page 175

**Clear
Rhinestone Brads**
113144 **$10.95**
page 174

**On Board
Timeless Type**
112083 $12.95
page 183

**1-3/4" Circle
Punch**
112004 $15.95
page 184

set of **6** | **Prehistoric Pals**
115048 $20.95

bark, bark, bark
(happy we're friends)

set of **6** | **Man's Best Friend**
113236 $19.95

The Teacher's Pet set is designed for use by teachers, but the versatile images can be used in many ways by omitting the greeting portion of the stamp. Don't miss the coordinating Décor Elements (page 192) images.

wild about you!

Wild about You | *set of*
115110 **$25.95** | 8

don't forget

please bee neater

purrrfect!

dog-gone great!

please complete

please sign and return

Teacher's Pet | *set of*
111554 **$18.95** | 6

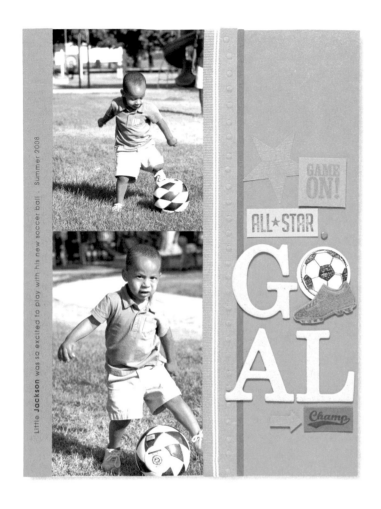

GOAL

set of 3 | **Just Soccer**
115010 $13.95

1ST DOWN

set of 3 | **Just Football**
115006 $13.95

SWISH

set of 3 | **Just Basketball**
115004 $13.95

BMX

set of 3 | **Just Riding**
115008 $13.95

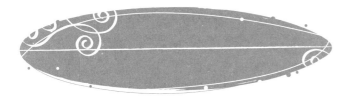

Just Surfing | set of
115012 **$13.95** | 3

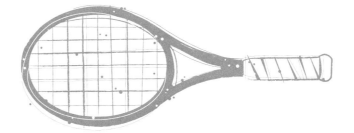

Just Tennis | set of
115014 **$13.95** | 3

Just Baseball | set of
115002 **$13.95** | 3

ALL★STAR   SCORE   ★   #1 MVP

GO TEAM!   Champ   GAME ON!

Sporting | set of
115072 **$18.95** | 8

Home and family time have never been more fun! Our All in the Family sets are so versatile, you'll never run out of ideas for using them. So gather the crew and create projects for all of your occasions and events.

You are invited to a
Karaoke Party!

Saturday, February 21, 2009
8:00 pm
at Mandy's House
2222 West Willow Lane

Bring your best singing voice
for a night of good food
and lots of fun!

. . . . let's celebrate . . . .

you're invited

set of 10 | **Family Accessories Too** | 113760 **$19.95**

set of 12 | **Family Accessories** | 113494 **$19.95**

thank you

i like you

you're invited

happy together

let's celebrate

happy new baby

from all of us

happy birthday

love you much

set of 9 | **Family Phrases** | 114960 **$19.95**

Button Latte
114333 **$7.95**
page 176

Flower Fusion Too
Accents & Elements
112006 **$14.95**
page 177

White
Stampin' Emboss® Powder
109132 **$4.75**
page 186

All in the Family
113488 **$38.95** | *set of* 28

Neighborhood
(jumbo) 109685 **$8.50**

**Chocolate Chip Patterns
Designer Series Paper**
112164 **$9.95**
page 159

**Chit Chat
Rub-Ons**
111804 **$10.95**
page 173

**Old Olive
5/8" Grosgrain Ribbon**
109054 **$7.95**
page 179

step 2
*Gently remove the ink
from portions of the wheel
with a baby wipe.*

step 4
*Breathe on the rubber to
remoisten the ink. Then, roll
the wheel across your paper
or card stock.*

step 3
*Brush the wide end of a
Stampin' Write® marker
on the uninked portion.*

step 1
*Ink the wheel with an ink
pad of your choice.*

stampin' around with ink & markers

You don't need a Stampin' Around ink cartridge for this technique. Instead, create multicolored wheeled images by
using an ink pad and marker. This technique allows you to emphasize certain words or images—any part of the wheel
you want to stand out. To learn about other Stampin' Around techniques, contact your demonstrator.

:: featured image ::
You'll find the stamp image shown above in the Friends 24-7 set (page 81).

all natural

:: WILDLIFE :: FLOWERS :: TREES ::

The way to **KNOW LIFE** is to **LOVE** *many things.*
—VAN GOGH

Kind Thanks

Flower Fancy
set of 10 | 111578 **$36.95**

The way to **KNOW LIFE**
is to **LOVE** *many things.*

—VAN GOGH

WE GROW GREAT BY
DREAMS
—WOODROW WILSON

Dreams du Jour
set of 4 | 111624 **$18.95**

On Board
Small Book Basics
110712 **$5.95**
page 183

Top Note
Big Shot Bigz Die
113463 **$21.95**
page 196

Valet
Ribbon Originals
114318 **$12.95**
page 178

The HAPPIEST business in the world is that of making **FRIENDS**
~Anne S. Eaton

{24-7}

♡ | **Friends 24-7** | *set of*
| 113218 **$25.95** | 6

No good thing is PLEASANT without FRIENDS to share it. ~Seneca

KINDRED SPIRITS

My FRIENDS Are My ESTATE. ~Emily Dickinson

true Friends, are hard to find, difficult to leave, and impossible to forget.

you've got a friend in me

true blue you

Confidant

When Friends are together, HEARTS speak without words. ~Woodrow Wilson

friendship is the only cement that will ever hold the world together.

SOULMATE

you & me friends
forever and ever

PALS

HEART TO HEART

♡ | **Friendly Words**
| *(jumbo)* 114696 **$8.50**

Parisian Breeze Specialty Designer Series Paper
113993 **$11.95**
page 158

Color Spritzer Tool
107066 **$12.95**
page 190

Kraft Taffeta Ribbon
109068 **$6.95**
page 179

Slit Punch
104388 **$5.95**
page 184

Bella Rose Designer Series Paper
112041 **$9.95**
page 159

Dress Up Ribbon Originals
114317 **$12.95**
page 178

Thank you for touching my life.

set of	**A Rose Is a Rose**
14	111560 **$37.95**

Your friendship is like a song of spring.

set of	**Spring Song**
3	115074 **$15.95**

Your friendship is like a song of spring.

It's not just for labels any more. Use our versatile Designer Label punch (page 184) to frame an image as featured on the Flower card.

May your HAPPILY EVER AFTER *begin with a beautiful today.*

Ever After | *set of* 4
113401 **$22.95**

Romance
115121 **$6.50**

IT'S TIME TO
Bloom

from our home
TO YOURS

Bella's Bloom | *set of* 4
111600 **$12.95**

Bella's Border
112476 **$6.50**

Pretties Kit
109114 **$29.95**
page 175

**Chateau Bella
Rub-Ons**
111416 **$10.95**
page 172

set of
9 | **Heartfelt Thanks**
114980 **$32.95**

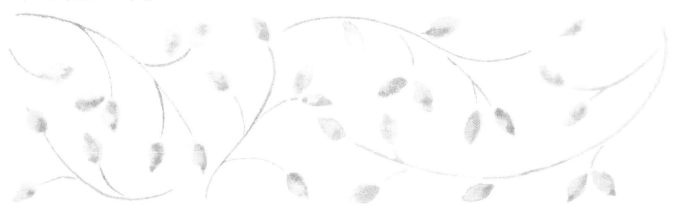

Watercolor Vine
107560 **$8.50** *(jumbo)*

blos•som (blŏs′əm) *n.*
1. A flower or cluster of
flowers. **2.** The condition
of flowering. **3a.** A time
of vigor, freshness, and
beauty. **b.** A period of
maximum development
and reaching possibilities.

Bloomin' Beautiful | *set of*
111490 **$25.95** | 5

Wonderful Watercolors | *set of*
(*double-mounted*) 113688 **$39.95** | 12

WITH SYMPATHY

KINDRED SPIRITS

WITH SYMPATHY

set of 4 | **Kindred Spirits**
111662 **$21.95** *(double mounted)*

ESP 112929 Almas gemelas

thanks so much

friend to friend

set of 6 | **Pocket Silhouettes**
111672 **$18.95**

happy
for you

you're
on my mind

Organic Outlines | set of
111670 **$24.95** | 4

BIRTHDAY
—CELEBRATIONS—

you're
on my mind

THANK YOU
. . . . . . FOR YOUR FRIENDSHIP

Upsy Daisy | set of
111710 **$18.95** | 4

set of
5 | **Doodle This**
114954 **$33.95**

Doodle
109684 **$8.50** (jumbo)

Whimsy
109688 **$8.50** (jumbo)

*Cut around the wings of a butterfly
to give it a slight touch of fun.
At first glance, the butterfly seems
to fly right off the card.*

HELLO

Kind Thanks

A Flower for All Seasons | set of
111592 **$14.95** | 4

best friends listen
to what you don't say

the time to be happy is now. the place to be happy is here.

Garden Whimsy | set of
113502 **$25.95** | 8

marvelous
wonderful
beautiful
perfect

Isabella,
It's been so
amazing to
see your
personality
grow and
flourish
through
the years.

May 2008

**Good Morning Sunshine
Designer Series Paper**
113966　**$9.95**
page 160

**Bright Delights
Rub-Ons**
113887　**$11.95**
page 172

set of **7**　**Petal Pizzazz**
113417　**$32.95**

a special note of thanks

you've got a friend in me!

hello there!

set of **11**　**Cheep Talk**
113204　**$26.95**

You've
got a
FRIEND
in me

wonderful

hello there!

friend

thinking of you

good
· · · · · friend

thinking of you

thanks so much

		Good Friend	*set of*
		113740 **$28.95**	8

	Trendy Trees	*set of*
	113258 **$17.95**	8

Funky Forest
114695 **$6.50**

A true friend reaches for your hand
and touches your heart.

---

set of 7	**Simple Friendship**
	113397 **$25.95**

Use our Fresh Cuts images with
the Fresh-Cut Notes (page 157). The
background image shows through
the cut-out flower portion to
create a beautiful focal point.

set of 5	**Fresh Cuts**
	111634 **$21.95**

Tearing card stock by hand adds texture to the *Embrace Life* card. Use The Tearing Edge® (page 189) when you want to create a uniform torn look.

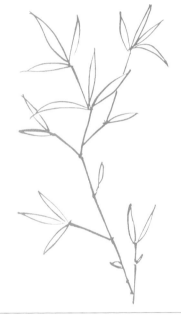

Embrace Life | *set of* 5
114958 **$25.95**

Pretty Amazing | *set of* 6
115050 **$22.95**

From hardware, to accessories, to Stampin' Dimensionals®—think of all the possibilities! Bring your creations to life with a little dimension.

Have a
happy
day!

life

Eastern Blooms
set of 5 | 111626 **$21.95**

A Beautiful Thing
set of 6 | 113618 **$20.95**

YOU MAKE MY *life* A BEAUTIFUL THING.

It's Beautiful
111201 **$8.50** *(jumbo)*

So Swirly
109683 **$8.50** *(jumbo)*

**Flock Together
Designer Series Paper**
114018 **$9.95**
page 161

**Tag Corner
Punch**
107215 **$6.95**
page 184

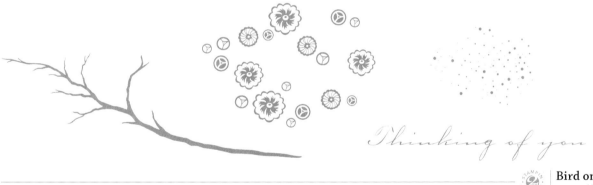

Bird on a Branch | set of
113266 **$18.95** | 5

Sweet Serenity
113835 **$6.50**

Eastern Influences | set of
111628 **$18.95** | 4

95

Morning Glory

It is not how much you do,
but how much love
you put into the doing
that matters.
~Mother Teresa

set of **Morning Soft**
2 | 115036 **$18.95**

thank you so much

set of **Best Kind of Friend**
7 | 114922 **$21.95**

Kraft Taffeta Ribbon
109068 **$6.95**
page 179

Aqua Painter
103954 **$16.95**
page 190

Earth Elements Brads
106955 **$8.95**
page 174

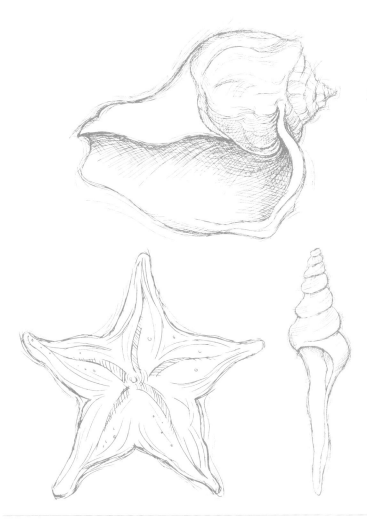

SUmMeR

2008

Candace and Marcel engagement photo shoot.

Seaside *set of* 5
113512 **$25.95**

Ocean Commotion *set of* 4
114423 **$17.95**

Linen Thread
104199 **$4.50**
page 179

Twill Tape
105245 **$5.95**
page 179

Spiral Punch
108341 **$10.95**
page 184

Stitched Exotics
set of 9 | 115080 $34.95

thank you so very much

Flight of the Butterfly
set of 10 | 111564 $31.95

ESP 112911 Vuelo de la mariposa

one person can make such a difference there would be no ~ if nothing ever changed butterflies. ~ unknown

hope your day is as happy as happy gets!

So Saffron
7/8" Poly–Twill Ribbon
111364 **$8.95**
page 179

Tea Party
Designer Series Paper
113992 **$9.95**
page 161

Playful Petals | *set of*
113728 **$28.95** | 7

Sweet Stems | *set of*
113726 **$16.95** | 4

LOVE, PEACE, JOY

thinking of you

set of 6 | **Lovely As a Tree**
115026 $27.95

always on my mind

set of 8 | **Branch Out**
113200 $22.95

Both sets on this page coordinate with the elegant Tailor Made Simply Scrappin' (page 163). Combine them to create eye-catching projects.

GOD writes the GOSPEL
not in the BIBLE alone, but
on TREES and FLOWERS
and CLOUDS and STARS.
~ Martin Luther

Le Jardin Botanique | *set of*
113232 $25.95 | **6**

Lexicon of Leaves | *set of*
113710 $25.95 | **5**

To pay homage to BEAUTY is to
admire NATURE; to admire nature
is to WORSHIP GOD.
—Unknown

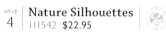

set of
4 | **Nature Silhouettes**
111542 **$22.95**

set of
5 | **Backwoods**
113407 **$23.95**

Hit the Road | *set of* 5
113242 $19.95

grrreat!

Skee-ter Spray

Under the Stars | *set of* 10
111556 $29.95

Skeeters
113118 $6.50

step 1
Pour a little bleach onto a folded paper towel.

step 2
"Ink" the stamp with the paper towel as if it were an ink pad.

step 3
Stamp the image.

step 4
Use our heat tool (page 186) to set the image.

stamping with bleach

Create a one-of-a-kind look by stamping with bleach instead of ink. This technique produces unique results on each color of card stock. Try it with different colors to see what you like best, then use it to create distinctive stamped images. No two are alike! Ask your demonstrator to show this technique at your next workshop.

:: *featured image* ::
You'll find the stamp image shown above in the Central Park set (page 106).

elements

You only live once,
but if you do it right,
once is enough.

set of 5 | **Fifth Avenue Floral**
113734 **$24.95**

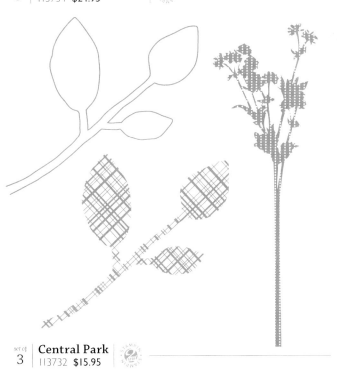

set of 3 | **Central Park**
113732 **$15.95**

**Kiwi Kiss
Corduroy Buttons**
114338 **$9.95**
page 176

**Taste of Textiles
Specialty Paper**
113991 **$9.95**
page 156

**Fashion District
Rub-Ons**
113884 **$10.95**
page 172

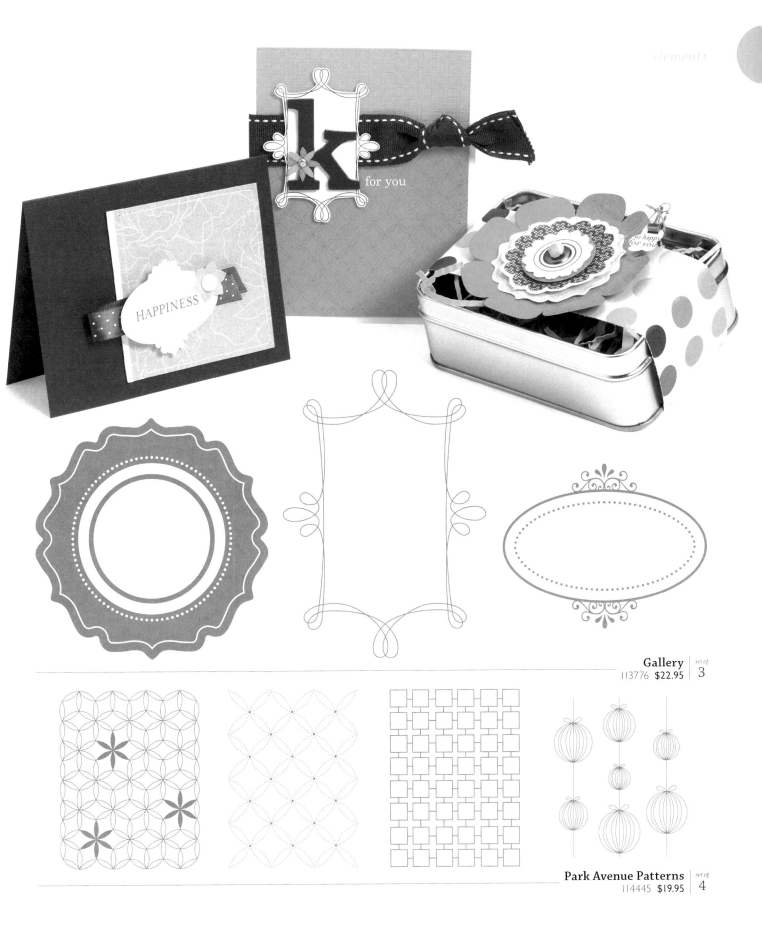

for you

HAPPINESS

Gallery | *set of* **3**
113776 **$22.95**

Park Avenue Patterns | *set of* **4**
114445 **$19.95**

Urban Oasis
Designer Series Paper
113978 **$9.95**
page 161

Canvas Cuts
Accents & Elements
113979 **$7.95**
page 177

Mini
Library Clips
109857 **$12.95**
page 176

Our paper-piercing template (available in the Crafters' Tool Kit, page 188) makes it easy to create uniform rows of pierced holes. This creates an intricate effect with little effort.

Frames with a Flourish
7 | 113496 **$34.95**

set of
6 | **Seeing Spots**
115058 **$16.95**

**Basic Black
1/4" Grosgrain Ribbon**
109027 **$4.95**
page 179

**Jackpot
Designer Series Paper**
113995 **$9.95**
page 159

YOU MAKE ME LAUGH

KING FOR A DAY

QUEEN OF EVERYTHING

Card Games | *set of* 3
113202 **$19.95**

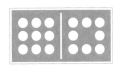

BIG WINNER!

game night

JACKPOT

Game Night | *set of* 8
113220 **$20.95**

In the Cards
113831 **$6.50**

1-3/8" Circle Punch
104401 **$15.95**
page 184

Sweet Slumber Specialty Designer Series Paper
114037 **$11.95**
page 158

Clips Assortment
112580 **$6.95**
page 176

set ct
6 | **True Friend**
110378 **$22.95**

 Boho Friend
110334 **$6.50**

WONDERFUL FRIEND

★ ★ ★ ★ ★ ★ ★ ★ ★ ★

YOU MAKE ME HAPPY

Boho Backgrounds | set of
114940 **$17.95** | 4

Wanted | set of
115106 **$23.95** | 8

Line your boxes with our Designer Series paper (pages 158–161), available in dozens of patterns and colors. With so many styles to choose from, you're sure to find one for any project.

love & HAPPINESS

cherish

kind

Baroque Motifs
set of 6 | 113490 $27.95

 Baroque Border
109675 $6.50

 Dazzling Diamonds Stampin' Glitter
102023 $4.50
page 180

 Chateau Bella Rub-Ons
111416 $10.95
page 172

 **Box #2 Big Shot Bigz XL Die**
114518 $34.95
page 194

always on my mind—
forever in my heart.

{EVERYTHING}

you mean everything to me.

Always | *set of*
113620 **$28.95** | 11

Always in Bloom
113834 **$6.50**

for you

{ YOU ARE *One*
OF A KIND }

One of a Kind | *set of*
113624 **$19.95** | 6

Bashful Blue
1" Double-Stitched
Grosgrain Ribbon
111848 **$8.95**
page 178

Chit Chat
Rub-Ons
111804 **$10.95**
page 173

Boho Blossoms
Punch
110711 **$15.95**
page 184

113

set of
11 | **Pick a Petal**
115042 **$29.95**

what can i say? you made my day!

i made a wish and you came true!

always on my mind - forever in my heart.

happy birthday · happy birthday

set of
4 | **Stem Sayings**
115078 **$20.95**

friendship · friendship friendship · friendship

happy thoughts · happy thoughts

happy birthday · happy birthday

thanks so much · thanks so much

set of
6 | **Think Happy Thoughts**
115092 **$16.95**

Many of our stamp sets and punches coordinate—like our Think Happy Thoughts set and circle punches. Cut your cutting time instead of your paper by using punches on your projects.

With so many circle accessories—
buttons, brads, eyelets, pretties,
and more—there's a center for every
flower you stamp or punch.

enjoy
every moment

thank you

enjoy
every moment

life

the little things

Enjoy Every Moment
113622 **$31.95** *set of* 11

Daisy Dash
(jumbo) 111255 **$8.50**

115

Music expresses
that which
cannot be said.
~ Victor Hugo

set of **Music Expressions**
2 | 113718 **$16.95**

Symphony
113832 **$8.50** *(jumbo)*

3/16" Corner Rounder Punch
109047 **$6.95**
page 184

Rich Regals Brads
106953 **$8.95**
page 174

Blender Pens
102845 **$9.95**
page 190

Layering card stocks and papers can provide additional color and interest for your creations and provide a border for your focal point. Add more variety by tearing or punching one or more edges.

ESP 112923 Iluminaciones

Illuminations | set of
114990 **$30.95** | 4

Illuminated
112475 **$6.50**

**Antique Brass
Build-A-Brad**
109108 **$9.95**
page 174

**Scallop Edge
Punch**
112091 **$15.95**
page 184

**Always Artichoke
1/4" Grosgrain Ribbon**
109035 **$4.95**
page 179

rubber baby
buggy bumpers

fan mail

hope you
perk up
soon

grateful
for you

sorry about that

picture
perfect

sew glad we're
friends

just my type

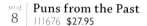

Puns from the Past
set of 8 | 111676 **$27.95**

with sympathy

warm wishes

thank you

forever friends

Beautiful Borders
set of 6 | 111594 **$25.95**

Small Oval Punch
107304 **$15.95**
page 184

Flower Fusion Too Accents & Elements
112006 **$14.95**
page 177

Valet Ribbon Originals
114318 **$12.95**
page 178

Classic Sketches | set of 3
113206 **$22.95**

Itty Bitty Backgrounds | set of 4
114996 **$14.95**

**Styled Silver
Hodgepodge Hardware**
111325 **$29.95**
page 175

**On Board
5" x 5" Art Journal**
108495 **$6.95**
page 183

**5-Petal Flower
Punch**
109041 **$15.95**
page 184

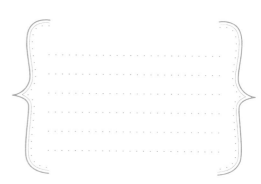

 Sweet Celebrations
set of 8 | 115082 **$24.95**

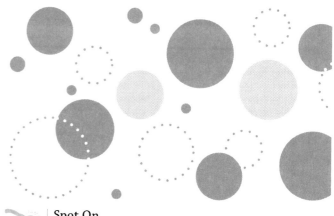

Dotted Lines
111256 **$8.50** (jumbo)

Spot On
107559 **$8.50** (jumbo)

 So Saffron
1/2" Striped
Grosgrain Ribbon
113699 **$7.95**
page 178

 Blooms Again
Die Cuts
112010 **$8.95**
page 181

 Summer Sun
Corduroy Buttons
114343 **$9.95**
page 176

FOR YOU

So*KIND

PRICELESS

PRICELESS

So*KIND

Priceless | *set of*
115052 **$28.95** | 11

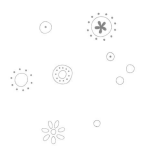

Sprinkles | *set of*
115076 **$14.95** | 4

Button Bouquet
112092 **$7.95**
page 176

**So Saffron Patterns
Designer Series Paper**
112152 **$9.95**
page 159

**Scallop Circle
Punch**
109043 **$15.95**
page 184

Alex Tyson
May 5th, 2008
Looking so grown-up
at Grandma's house

baby

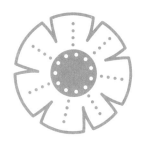

set of **8** | **Big Flowers**
114932 **$32.95**

thanks
hi
CONGRATS
HAPPY BIRTHDAY
CONGRATS

set of **4** | **Four Square**
111632 **$14.95**

set of **6** | **Little Flowers**
115020 **$11.95**

Little Bits
109691 **$6.50**

**Fresh Favorites II
Buttons**
107422 **$6.95**
page 176

**Washington Apple
Designer Series Paper**
112461 **$9.95**
page 161

**1-1/4" Circle
Punch**
104403 **$15.95**
page 184

 breads

 desserts

 veggies, salads & sides

 soups, stews & sauces

 misc.

 meats & main & dishes

yum scale

from the kitchen of:

From the Kitchen of | *set of* 9
114964 **$29.95**

Tart & Tangy | *set of* 4
111514 **$12.95**

Pig Tails
Ribbon Originals
114316 **$13.95**
page 178

On Board
Lots of Letters
109182 **$12.95**
page 183

Flower Assortment
Designer Brads
112583 **$6.95**
page 175

Wide Oval Punch
112082 **$15.95**
page 184

5/16" Neutrals Brads
112534 **$7.95**
page 174

Clear Buttons
105447 **$4.95**
page 176

Totally Tabs *set of* 4
113520 **$17.95**

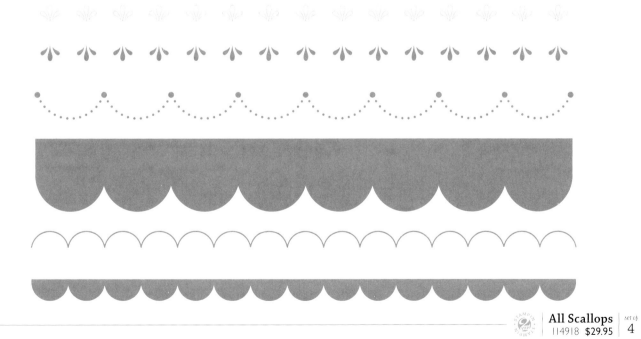

All Scallops *set of* 4
114918 **$29.95**

Round Tab Punch
108340 **$15.95**
page 184

Dress Up Ribbon Originals
114317 **$12.95**
page 178

Scallop Edge Punch
112091 **$15.95**
page 184

set of
4 | **Sweet Sampler**
115084 **$17.95**

january   april   july   october

february   may   august   november

march   june   september   december

set of
12 | **Full Calendar**
114966 **$17.95** *(double-mounted)*

set of
13 | **Mark the Date**
115034 **$26.95**

PRACTICE

Cute Cues | set of
111622 **$11.95** | 6

On Board
13" x 7-1/2" Clipboard
109192 **$15.95**
page 183

Raspberry Tart
Designer Series Paper
113975 **$9.95**
page 160

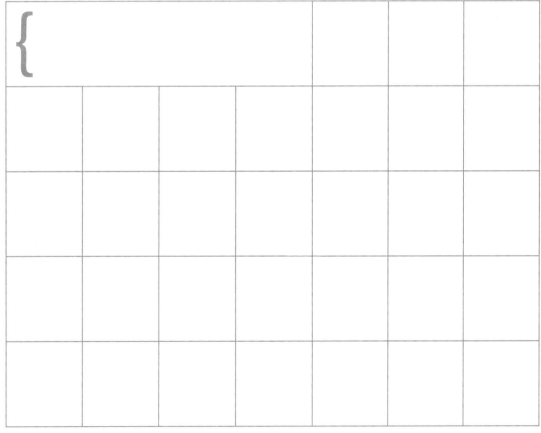

Calendar | set of
109298 **$17.95** | 1

127

Approximate dimensions for all background stamps are 4-1/2" x 5-3/4". The Gratuitous Graffiti stamp is shown at actual size. All other background stamps show the full image at 45%, with a small portion of the image at actual size.

Classic Stripes
111568 **$17.95**

Gratuitous Graffiti
111636 **$17.95**

Pretty Petals
111008 **$17.95**

Sanded | set of
109294 $17.95 | 1

Classifieds | set of
111616 $17.95 | 1

Baroque | set of
109264 $17.95 | 1

Très Chic | set of
109258 $17.95 | 1

Bella Toile | set of
111598 $17.95 | 1

En Français | set of
109521 $17.95 | 1

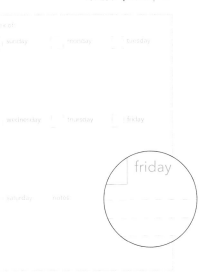

It's a Plan | set of
(double-mounted) 111658 $26.95 | 2

Boho Blooms | set of
111608 $17.95 | 1

step 1

Place paper or photo on glass mat, and tape at least two sides to hold in place.

step 2

Center base over project, and turn dial to select circle size.

step 3

Hold base steady. Push down cutting handle and turn in either direction.

step 4

Adjust to a slightly larger circle size and repeat steps to create ring.

using the circle scissor plus

Cutting circles has never been easier. Your demonstrator can show you how to use the Circle Scissor Plus to cut or draw perfect circles as small as 1" and up to 6" in diameter. With this cutting tool and Stampin' Up!'s circle punches, you'll have all the circle sizes you'll ever need!

:: featured image ::
You'll find the stamp images shown above in the Contempo Alphabet set (page 144).

good for you!

miss you already...

hey there!

so sorry you're sick

my fabulous friend

you're invited

thanks a gazillion

Really Retro
set of 7 | 113754 $14.95

Wonderful   happiness   adorable

Welcome   giggle   be merry

cherish   sparkle

Warm Words
set of 8 | 115108 $21.95

I just heard!   you're absolutely fabulous   you're so thoughtful

congrats on your big news!   No, seriously — you are!   thanks for all you do

In good times or bad   I'm there for you

Absolutely Fabulous
set of 8 | 114914 $21.95

celebrate

GOOD TIMES   YOUR DAY   YOU   LIFE

FRIENDSHIP   TIME TO   TODAY

Celebrate Everything
set of 8 | 114942 $18.95

YOUR DAY

thanks

Hello

I love you

Happy Birthday   Good Luck   Warm Wishes

Outlined for Fun | set ct 6
115038 $25.95

A NOTE OF THANKS

Kind Thanks

Thank You Kindly | set ct 4
111700 $13.95

Wonderful   favorite

niece   and   friend   husband   to a   mother   -in-law

nephew   son   grand   brother   aunt   father   sister

uncle   step   cousin   to my   wife   daughter   couple

Wonderful Favorites | set ct 23
115114 $40.95

133

Blessings brighten
when we count them!

THANK YOU
for blessing my life
in such a
wonderful way!

A friend is someone who
strengthens you
with prayers,
blesses you with love,
and encourages you
with hope.

May God's love
heal your sorrow, and may
His peace replace your
heartache with
warm and loving memories.

Today is God's gift
to you ...
Each day you are God's gift
to me!

May the God of love
be the heart
of your marriage,
the light of your home, and
the ever-present partner
in your new life
together.

Sharing with you
the miracle of
new hope and new life
through the glorious gift of
Christ the Lord.

A baby is a gift from
heaven above—
bringing joy down to earth,
filling hearts full of love.

May the miracle
of Christmas
find you safe in the
Peace of God,
warm in the
Light of Christ.

HAPPY BIRTHDAY

God's Blessings
set of 8 | 114972 **$33.95**

Birthday
hugs and wishes

You're invited

time:

place:

date:

rsvp:

Happy Anniversary

congratulations

Warm wishes

Hugs & Wishes
set of 6 | 114986 **$18.95**

HOLIDAY
Greetings

THANKS
So much

YOU'RE
Invited

Thinking
OF YOU

hope happens

tags

Birthday

Get well
SOON

Good
LUCK

BEST
wishes

Birthday
WISHES

Sincere Salutations | set of
115068 **$23.95** | 8

It takes COURAGE
to grow up
and become who you
REALLY are.

hope happens.

Do not put off till
TOMORROW
what can be
Enjoyed
TODAY.
~Josh Billings

Plant your feet firmly and
let your heart have wings.

Whoever is happy will make
others happy too. ~Anne Frank

Hope Happens | set of
113722 **$19.95** | 5

Birthday
Wishes

Just a
Note

All the
Best

For my
Friend

Holiday
Cheer

Many
Thanks

Elegant Cheer | set of
114956 **$18.95** | 6

FRIEND. GOOD.
—Frankenstein

What if the
HOKEY POKEY
really is
what it's ALL about?

If at first you don't succeed,
find out
if the loser gets anything.
~Bill Lyon

BE YOURSELF.

Nobody is better
qualified!

You're never too old
to do GOOFY stuff.
~Ward Cleaver

You're one of the
GOOD ones!
• • • • • • • • • • •

set of 6 | **Smarty Pants**
115070 **$18.95**

you, you, you

i miss you

i love you

Three little words...

thanks so much

so very sorry

thinking of you

set of 8 | **Three Little Words**
113254 **$13.95** *(double-mounted)*

'tis the season to
SPARKLE
believe

live each day with
LAUGHTER
enthusiasm

a perfect moment is
SERENDIPITY
sweet

find reasons to
CELEBRATE
be happy

a once in a lifetime
ADVENTURE
opportunity

you + me =
FRIENDSHIP
priceless

set of 9 | **Sweet Serendipity**
113626 **$20.95**

 best wishes   *thank you*   ⚲ *welcome baby*

♡ *love you*   🧁 *wish big*   ❄ *very merry*

Short & Sweet | set ct **12**
115060 $18.95

HOLIDAYS   DAYS   *happy*

EVERYTHING   BIRTHDAY

LIFE   FOR YOU   TOGETHER

Happy Everything | set ct **8**
115235 $17.95

just the **2** of us   **happy days**   E U R E K A !

·····my·little·buttercup·····   Many happy returns   you take the cake

head **over** heels   twist & shout   *tickled pink*

◉◉◉◉◉◉◉◉◉   have your cake and eat it too   lickety-split

HONEYBUN   Fancy Free   ✳ ✳ ✳ ✳ ✳ ✳ ✳

you're my only one   *Fabulous*

sending you my love   life's **too** short   happy as a clam

sweetie cakes   sunny side of the street   in stitches

~ HEART'S CONTENT ~   GOOD TIMES   ✳ **fancy pants** ✳

a **sight** for **sore** eyes   let your hair down

Many Happy Returns | set ct **3**
115032 $18.95

137

CAUTION
MILESTONE AHEAD

CALL
ME
ANY
TIME
←→

WAY TO GO! →

YOU'RE #
1

↻ ROCK

NEVER
STOP
BELIEVING

BE
PREPARED
TO PARTY

set of 7 | **It's a Sign**
114994 $30.95

kindness
comes in many forms but always from the heart.

may all your *wishes* come true!

welcome *christmas* into your heart.

wishing you *happiness* today & always.

set of 4 | **Heard from the Heart**
111644 $22.95

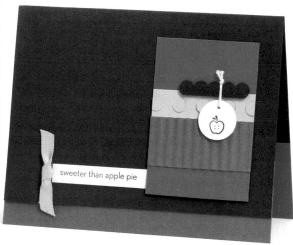

FRIEND	WISHES	LOVE	HAPPY
TO MY	CHRISTMAS	SO SORRY	BIRTHDAY
HELLO	NEW BABY	THANKS	WITH JOY
PARTY	EVERYTHING	FOREVER	ANNIVERSARY
FAMILY	CONGRATS	XOXOXO	GOOD LUCK
HI THERE	FOR YOU	MR. & MRS.	CELEBRATE

ESP 112917 Frases básicas

Fundamental Phrases *set of* **24**
(double-mounted) 114968 **$37.95**

 one smart cookie   you take the cake   orange you cute

 cool as a cucumber   sweeter than apple pie   thanks a bunch

One Smart Cookie *set of* **12**
111506 **$19.95**

Wishing you love and laughter... forever after!

I'm here for you always... please know that I care.

Two simple words that come with so much gratitude...thank you.

One little baby... many happy hearts!

You're a wonderful reason to celebrate!

If wishes could make you well... you'd be better already!

Time passes... friendship stays right where it's put!

Sending you a little something wrapped in a whole lot of love!

Curvy Verses *set of* **8**
114948 **$23.95**

GOOD LUCK
(circle all that apply)

HOPE IT TURNS OUT WELL

NO ONE DESERVES IT MORE

I KNOW YOU CAN DO IT

IT CAN ONLY GET BETTER

Have I told you lately...

☐ Hello

☐ I miss you

☐ I love you

☐ All of the above

xoxo

date

Dear _____.
     name

I just wanted to say sorry for

_____. It was all my
     verb

fault. I was a _____
                 noun

Please forgive me.

                 Sincerely,

_____
     name

HaPPY BiRTHDaY!
celebrate your day with . . .

10-something candles

20-something candles

30-something candles

40-something candles

1 fire extinguisher

CONGRATULATIONS ON...

⇨ Your graduation   ⇨ The new baby

⇨ Being so cool   ⇨ Your wedding

⇨ Your new job   ⇨ Your retirement

set of 5 | **In Good Form** | 111654 $29.95

just fabulous

is for

CUZ Baby happy

yourself way to

is for

Birthday Mine

B

set of 12 | **Just B** | 115000 $29.95

Happy Birthday!

LIVE, LAUGH & LOVE

happy birthday

on your
BIRTHDAY...

Just thinking of you on your birthday!

look who's
turning

( )

happy o' birthday

birthday
GREETINGS

(A little late!)

I just wanted to give you
a reason to celebrate
a **little** longer!
Happy Belated Birthday

wishing you the
HAPPIEST
birthday yet!

let's
celebrate!

It's your day...
ENJOY!

On Your Birthday | set of 12
111664 $33.95

Lovely Labels | set of 4
115028 $14.95

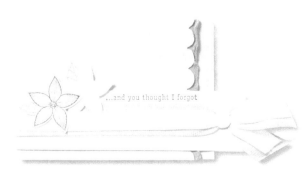

...and you thought I forgot

{ make a wish }

CELEBRATE **YOU**   H A P P Y   B I R T H D A Y

A Little Birthday Cheer | set of 4
115018 $13.95

**Styled Silver
Hodgepodge Hardware**
111325 **$29.95**
page 175

MADE WITH LOVE
© STAMPIN' UP!

limited edition

**Chocolate Chip
1" Double-Stitched
Grosgrain Ribbon**
111849 **$8.95**
page 178

HAND STAMPED
© STAMPIN' UP!

PHOTOGRAPH BY

art { *original design* }

Created by:
© STAMPIN' UP!

---

set of **8** | **Art by Design**
114920 **$17.95**

ESP 112891 Arte y diseño

Thank You
) *for your order* (

limited

wish list

TO DO:
☐
☐
☐
☐
☐

Phone me
to place an order

Special

GIRLS'
NIGHT
OUT

new! { A *Fabulous* GIFT FOR YOU }

please come

THANKS
your order is appreciated

---

set of **11** | **Taking Care of Business**
115090 **$25.95**

Save the Date
JOIN US FOR THE CELEBRATION
Suzie & Matt's wedding
EVENT
August 10, 2009
DATE
Kaui, Hawaii
LOCATION

Celebrate!

In Honor of:

Date:

Time:

Place:

Registered:

You're Invited!

For

When

At

PLEASE COME

party for

date

place

surprise ☐

host

rsvp

Save the Date

JOIN US FOR THE CELEBRATION

.... EVENT

.... DATE

.... LOCATION

Please Come | set ct
115046 **$25.95** | 5

INTRODUCING...

it's a boy!

.... FOR

.... DATE

.... TIME

.... PLACE

.... RSVP

INTRODUCING...

SAVE THE DATE

you're
INVITED

Introducing | set ct
114443 **$15.95** | 4

143

alphabets

Create your own tags, scrapbook titles, framed pictures, and more with our alphabets, available in many styles and sizes. Now it's easier than ever to customize your projects with a name, date, or other message.

The double-mounted alphabet and number sets are designed to mount two per block, one on each side. This helps save space when you store your stamps.

The Big Deal, Jumbo Outline, and Schoolbook Serif Alphabets include 24 stamps, with "b" used as "q," "d" used as "p," and "n" used as "u" when stamped upside-down. Calendar Alphabet & Numbers uses "n" as "u" when stamped upside-down. The Big Deal, Short Order, and Taffy Numbers use the "6" as "9" when stamped upside-down.

AaBb&*?{

Short Order Alphabet
set of 56 | 115062 **$42.95** *(double-mounted)*

AaBb?!&⚹

Ticker Tape Alphabet
set of 56 | 115096 **$42.95** *(double-mounted)*

012345
678#—
nd rd no. st th

Short Order Numbers
set of 24 | 115064 **$27.95** *(double-mounted)*

a b c
& and
no.

123456789
012345678
901234567
890123456
789012345

Contempo Alphabet
set of 30 | 111570 **$42.95** *(double-mounted)*

Jumbo Outline Alphabet
set of 24 | 114998 **$42.95** *(double-mounted)*

Varsity Alphabet | set of
(double-mounted) 113684 **$43.95** | 26

Varsity Numbers | set of
(double-mounted) 113686 **$24.95** | 12

Taffy Alphabet | set of
(double-mounted) 115086 **$43.95** | 28

Taffy Numbers | set of
(double-mounted) 115088 **$24.95** | 12

Big Deal Alphabet | set of
(double-mounted) 114928 **$42.95** | 24

Big Deal Numbers | set of
(double-mounted) 114930 **$24.95** | 12

Schoolbook Serif Alphabet | set of
(double-mounted) 113510 **$42.95** | 24

Schoolbook Serif Numbers | set of
(double-mounted) 111680 **$24.95** | 12

Creating a cover for your On Board Art Journal (page 183) is easy with our Spiral punch (page 184). The alignment guide creates evenly spaced holes that slide right onto the cover.

ABC Images
set of 28 | 114912 $34.95

ABC Alphabet Lower
set of 28 | 114908 $29.95

ABC Alphabet Upper
set of 28 | 114910 $29.95

My ABCs
109568 $6.50

Aa Bb Cc Dd Ee Ff
Gg Hh Ii Jj Kk Ll
Mm Nn Oo Pp Qq Rr
Ss Tt Uu Vv Ww Xx
Yy Zz

a *little* LETTER *for you!*

FULL SET SHOWN AT 40%   ACTUAL SIZE

Aa

Defining Alphabet | *set of*
(double-mounted) 114952 **$43.95** | 28

al•ways : {ôl'wāz} *adv.*
Every minute of every day.
Forever; unchanging. At all
times; invariably.

---

al•ways : {ôl'wāz} *adv.*
Every minute of every day.
Forever; unchanging. At all
times; invariably.

eve•ry•thing :
All things that are essential to you. All that you know; the whole world.

in•spire :
To cause or create new ideas. Fresh thought; to influence. To motivate to action.

mem•or•ies :
Recollection of the past; reminiscing and recalling experiences. Treasured good times; fond.

qual•i•ty :
Well made or superior. Top of the line; excellent; high class. To provide the best.

u•nique :
Being the only one of its kind. Unusual; extraordinary. Unlike any other; having no equal.

you :
The one and only; the one I treasure very much; to cherish. The person in my thoughts.

be•cause :
And because for a reason; the reason being "Because I love you," or "Because you're worth it."

fa•vor•ite :
Something regarded with special favor or liking. Best rated; preferred above all others.

jour•ney :
An experience or process that involves ever-changing; trail of experience. From here to there.

near•ly :
In a close manner; intimately. Almost but not quite; nearly everything. So very close.

re•mem•ber :
To keep in mind or worthy of remembrance or recognition. Memories of days gone by.

ver•y :
To a high degree; extremely. Truly. To reminisce a good quality. "You are very *special*."

zeal :
Enthusiastic devotion to a cause; ideal or goal. Passion; energy; zest for life.

cre•ate :
To produce through artistic or imaginative effort. Create and inspire. To make your own.

grat•i•tude :
State of happiness or joy. Expressing appreciation for something or someone.

kind•ness :
Goodness for the sake of being good. Warmhearted and considerate. Acts of kindness.

or•i•gin•al :
Fresh and inventive. One of a kind; unique; first in its class. Work of heart. "Be *original*."

sim•ple :
Joy in little things without pretense or show. In a plain or unadorned way; in a snap.

wish :
Heart's desire; to dream of much but aspire to. To want. "Wish upon a star."

[DEFINE *your* life!]

de•light :
A high degree of enjoyment. Expressions of joy; extreme satisfaction. "You are a *delight*."

hap•py :
Cheerful; tickled pink; content. Simple pleasure; together. A feeling of gladness or joy.

lu•cky :
Fortune smiles upon you. Favored with special circumstances. Lucky you; just lucky.

per•fect :
Lacking nothing essential to the whole; giving your best. Flawless; admirable; just right.

to•geth•er :
You and me; lonely no more. With another; inseparable. In harmony; in sync.

x•o•x•o :
Hugs and kisses; love and affection. Closing or salutation of a love note sealed with love.

FULL SET SHOWN AT 40%   ACTUAL SIZE

Define Your Life | *set of*
(double-mounted) 114950 **$47.95** | 28

ACTUAL SIZE | FULL SET SHOWN AT 40%

set of **30** | **Lovely Letters**
115030 **$42.95** *(double-mounted)*

ACTUAL SIZE | FULL SET SHOWN AT 40%

set of **30** | **Wild West Alphabet**
115112 **$42.95** *(double-mounted)*

A B C D E F G H I J K L M
N O P Q R S T U V W X Y Z {
: 0 1 2 3 4 5 6 7 8 ❄ @ ? ! &
♦ ❀ ✿ ♥ ● ▶ ★ ■ Nº ¼ ½ ¾ % $

set of **56** | **Simple Serif Mini Alphabet & Numbers***
109429 **$20.95** *(double-mounted)*

a b c d e f g h i j k l m n o p q r s t v
w x y z 1 2 3 4 5 6 7 8 9 10 11 12 13 14 15
16 17 18 19 20 21 22 23 24 25 26 27 28 29 30 31

set of **56** | **Calendar Alphabet & Numbers***
111610 **$20.95** *(double-mounted)*

When you assemble the stamps in the mini alphabet sets, two stamps go on each wood block, with one at each end. Put the clear label on the blocks first to guide you when positioning the stamps.

personalized stamps

Stamp your personal belongings and correspondence with Stampin' Up!'s personalized stamps.
Choose from seven designs to create a stamp that meets your needs.

The "Hand Stamped By" personalized name stamps below fulfill the requirements of Stampin' Up!'s angel policy, which governs the sale of hand-stamped items. For more information, contact your demonstrator or go to www.stampinup.com.

Personalized stamps must be ordered using special forms. Ask your demonstrator for assistance. Please note: No returns can be accepted on personalized stamps.

Large Text-Only Stamps
Choose either 1 or 2 lines of text, up to 16 characters per line. Spaces count as a character; capitals count as 2 spaces.

Simple Serif

104536	Simple Serif One-Line*	$13.95
104537	Simple Serif Two-Line*	$15.95

Name Here
(123) 456-7890

Text-and-Image Stamps
Choose either 3 or 4 lines of text, up to 32 characters per line. Spaces count as a character; capitals count as 2 spaces. Font styles and images cannot be interchanged.

Best Bee

104533	Best Bee Three-Line	$18.95
104532	Best Bee Four-Line	$20.95

First & Last Name
1234 Your Street
City, State 12345
(123) 456-7890

Elegant Flower

104529	Elegant Flower Three-Line	$18.95
104528	Elegant Flower Four-Line	$20.95

First & Last Name
1234 Your Street
City, State 12345
(123) 456-7890

Text-Only Stamps
Choose from 1-4 lines of text, up to 32 characters per line. Spaces count as a character; capitals count as 2 spaces.

Classic

104541	Classic One-Line	$10.95
104540	Classic Two-Line	$13.95
104539	Classic Three-Line	$15.95
104538	Classic Four-Line	$17.95

First & Last Name
1234 Your Street
City, State 12345
(123) 456-7890

Contemporary

104545	Contemporary One-Line	$10.95
104544	Contemporary Two-Line	$13.95
104543	Contemporary Three-Line	$15.95
104542	Contemporary Four-Line	$17.95

First & Last Name
1234 Your Street
City, State 12345
(123) 456-7890

"Hand Stamped By" Stamps
One line of personalized text (for name, in all caps), up to 16 capital letters. Spaces count as a character.

Decorative Design

104535	Decorative Design	$18.95

Tag It

103516	Tag It	$18.95

step 1

Remove white liner from Sticky Cut.

step 2

Place Sticky Cut where you want it on your project. Apply pressure to secure image, and then remove red liner.

step 3

Cover entire image with glitter.

step 4

Lift project and tap off excess glitter.

using sticky cuts with glitter

Sticky Cuts (page 180) are die-cut, double-sided adhesive images made from the same material as Sticky Strip. Sticky Cuts are one of the easiest ways to adhere Stampin' Glitter, Bead Duo, or Micro beads (page 180) to your project in the shape of Stampin' Up! exclusive images. Let your demonstrator show you how to make your projects shine!

:: *featured image* ::
You'll find the stamp image shown above in the Sweet Stems set (page 99).

accessories

:: CARD STOCK :: INK :: EMBELLISHMENTS ::

color coordination

Whether you have a color scheme in mind or want to see our complete line of colors, you're in the right place! The next four pages list the products you can purchase in our exclusive colors.

Stampin' Up!'s exclusive 80 lb., high-quality card stock is dyed with pure color all the way through. Available as color family assortments and as individual color packages. Acid and lignin free, buffered *sm*

Our ink pads feature feature a flip-top design that stores the inking surface upside-down, so it stays moist between re-inkings. Use our Classic Stampin' Pads when you need fast-drying, dye based inks. Our Craft Stampin' Pads contain rich pigment inks that are ideal for scrapbooking, embossing, and other craft projects.

sm   While most of Stampin' Up!'s products are safe for your scrapbooks, our Stampin' Memories symbol identifies those that were specifically created for and are the best choice for scrapbooking.

   The new icon marks new accessories.

Stampin' Write Markers

Set of 48 Stampin' Write dual-tip markers. Horizontal storage case keeps both tips inked evenly.

105541	Many Marvelous Markers	$125.95
105538	Bold Brights (12)	$31.95
105539	Earth Elements (12)	$31.95
105540	Rich Regals (12)	$31.95
105537	Soft Subtles (12)	$31.95
109126	Neutrals (4)**	$10.95

Watercolor Pencils

Made with deep pigments, our brilliantly colored pencils come in a sturdy tin container. Use alone to color stamped images or use with a blender pen, watercolor brushes, or Aqua Painter for lovely effects. Acid free. 24 assorted colors. *sm*

101879	Watercolor Pencils	$19.95

Stampin' Pastels

Protected in a sturdy case complete with 6 applicators and an eraser. Acid free.

105542	Stampin' Pastels®	$24.95

Watercolor Wonder™ Crayons

Water-soluble and easy-to-blend crayons in Stampin' Up!'s exclusive colors allow for an almost unlimited range of shades. *sm*

106695	Bold Brights (12)	$19.95
106696	Earth Elements (12)	$19.95
106698	Rich Regals (12)	$19.95
106697	Soft Subtles (12)	$19.95
106746	Neutrals (6)	$9.95

In Color

In Color	Classic stampin' pad $5.95	Classic ink refill $2.95	card stock 8-1/2" x 11" (24 sheets) $5.50	card stock 12" x 12"	card stock 12" x 12" textured	ribbon striped $9.95
PACIFIC POINT	111837	111840	111350	–	–	111370
BAJA BREEZE	111833	111844	111352	–	–	111375
KIWI KISS	111835	111842	111353	–	–	111372
RIDING HOOD RED	111836	111839	111348	–	–	111374
PINK PIROUETTE	111838	111843	111351	–	–	111373
TANGERINE TANGO	111834	111841	111349	–	–	111371
assorted			36 sheets (6 ea. of 6 colors) $7.95	24 sheets (4 ea. of 6 colors) $8.95	24 sheets (4 ea. of 6 colors) $11.95	
IN COLOR	–	–	111347	111346	111345	–

Colors, item numbers, and prices for items available in our color families are listed on pages 153–155. Don't miss any of these additional coordinating products:

Note Cards (page 157)
Designer Series Paper (pages 158–161)
Simply Scrappin' (pages 162–165)
Simply Sent® (pages 166–171)
Accents & Elements (page 177)
Ribbon (pages 178–179)
Die Cuts (page 181)
Albums (page 187)

neutrals

neutrals	Classic stampin' pad $5.95	Classic ink refill $2.95	markers stampin' write $3.25	Craft stampin' pad $7.50	Craft ink refill $4.25	card stock 8-1/2" x 11" (40 sheets) $7.50	card stock 12" x 12" (20 sheets) $7.50	card stock 12" x 12" textured	cartridges standard cartridge $5.25	cartridges jumbo cartridge $7.50
WHISPER WHITE	–	–	–	101731	101780	100730	106529	–	–	–
VERY VANILLA	–	–	–	104308	104328	101650	106530	–	–	–
SAHARA SAND	105208	105220	105105	–	–	105328	106531	–	–	–
BASIC BROWN	104315*	104314*	–	–	–	–	–	–	–	–
GOING GRAY	103274	102521	–	–	–	–	–	–	–	–
BASIC GRAY	109120*	109121*	–	–	–	108692	108691	–	–	–
BASIC BLACK	101179*	102512*	100082	102192	102995	102851	106532	–	104581*	104582*
assorted			(set of 4)** $10.95			36 sheets (6 ea. of 6 colors)*** $7.95	24 sheets (4 ea. of 6 colors)*** $8.95	24 sheets (4 ea. of 6 colors)*** $11.95		
NEUTRALS	–	–	109126	–	–	108588	108589	108693	–	–

Color Coach

Our double-sided Color Coach features coordinating and complementary color suggestions for our exclusive colors, plus a convenient chart of neutral and monochromatic color choices.

105796   Color Coach® $9.95

Idea Book & Catalog

The Idea Book & Catalog offers more than 200 pages of Stampin' Up! stamp sets, accessories, and product ideas—all at your fingertips. With hundreds of full-color samples, the Idea Book & Catalog is packed with inspiration you can use again and again!

115246   Spring-Summer 2009 $9.95

*BASIC BROWN, BASIC BLACK, AND BASIC GRAY CLASSIC INKS ARE WATERPROOF.
**BASIC BLACK, SAHARA SAND, GOING GRAY, BASIC GRAY
***WHISPER WHITE, VERY VANILLA, SAHARA SAND, GOING GRAY, BASIC BLACK, BASIC GRAY

accessories

bold brights

	Classic stampin' pad $5.95	Classic ink refill $2.95	markers stampin' write $3.25	Craft stampin' pad $7.50	Craft ink refill $4.25	card stock 8-1/2" x 11" (24 sheets) $5.50	card stock 12" x 12" (20 sheets) $7.50	card stock 12" x 12" textured	cartridges standard cartridge $5.25	cartridges jumbo cartridge $7.50
GLORIOUS GREEN	103040	101453	100047	101436	100434	101697	106539	–	102212	103676
	102122	101735	100048	101325	102772	101768	107110	–	–	–
GABLE GREEN	101673	101483	100049	101671	101232	102795	107109	–	–	–
YOYO YELLOW	102717	101986	100050	101608	103325	102824	107108	–	–	–
ONLY ORANGE	102696	102931	100051	101951	102111	102837	107107	–	–	–
REAL RED	103133	103287	100052	101190	102104	102482	106545	–	102996	103675
PINK PASSION	101212	102308	100053	102916	103036	102762	107106	–	–	–
PIXIE PINK	105212	105224	105112	105236	105150	105121	107105	–	105203	–
ORCHID OPULENCE	101859	101324	100055	101900	100464	100969	107104	–	–	–
LOVELY LILAC	102874	103077	100056	102965	101695	100427	106541	–	–	103677
BRILLIANT BLUE	100691	100763	100057	101843	103006	100721	106540	–	100871	103674
	100814	101041	100058	100741	100957	102067	107103	–	101199	–

assorted

	Classic (set of 12) $57.95	Classic (set of 12) $28.95	markers (set of 12) $31.95	Craft (set of 12) $80.95	Craft (set of 12) $45.95	36 sheets (3 ea. of 12 colors) $7.95	24 sheets (2 ea. of 12 colors) $8.95	24 sheets (2 ea. of 12 colors) $11.95	stampin' spots Classic (set of 12) $22.50	stampin' spots Craft (set of 12) $25.95
BOLD BRIGHTS	105562	105554	105538	105558	105443	105548	106528	108698	105550	105439

earth elements

	Classic stampin' pad $5.95	Classic ink refill $2.95	markers stampin' write $3.25	Craft stampin' pad $7.50	Craft ink refill $4.25	card stock 8-1/2" x 11" (24 sheets) $5.50	card stock 12" x 12" (20 sheets) $7.50	card stock 12" x 12" textured	cartridges standard cartridge $5.25	cartridges jumbo cartridge $7.50
CHOCOLATE CHIP	100908	101065	100071	101816	102847	102128	107102	–	102496	–
CLOSE TO COCOA	103139	102444	100072	100549	100925	101341	107101	–	100714	–
CREAMY CARAMEL	103220	101478	100078	103034	102004	102514	106536	–	–	–
MORE MUSTARD	103162	101962	100076	103092	101990	100946	106542	–	–	103672
PUMPKIN PIE	105216	105229	105115	105240	105164	105117	107100	–	105200	–
REALLY RUST	102549	100685	100073	102437	103014	100661	107099	–	–	–
RUBY RED	102259	100532	100075	101009	102448	102030	106537	–	–	103673
CAMEO CORAL	103035	102238	100074	101933	101033	100475	107098	–	–	–
SUMMER SUN	100537	101231	100077	101690	102765	103124	107097	–	–	–
OLD OLIVE	102277	100531	100079	103063	101425	100702	106544	–	–	103670
GARDEN GREEN	102272	102059	100080	101841	100519	102584	107096	–	–	–
NOT QUITE NAVY	103008	102949	100059	103227	102310	101722	107095	–	–	–

assorted

	Classic (set of 12) $57.95	Classic (set of 12) $28.95	markers (set of 12) $31.95	Craft (set of 12) $80.95	Craft (set of 12) $45.95	36 sheets (3 ea. of 12 colors) $7.95	24 sheets (2 ea. of 12 colors) $8.95	24 sheets (2 ea. of 12 colors) $11.95	stampin' spots Classic (set of 12) $22.50	stampin' spots Craft (set of 12) $25.95
EARTH ELEMENTS	105563	105555	105539	105559	105442	105566	106527	108697	105551	105438

rich regals

	Classic		markers	Craft		card stock			cartridges	
	stampin' pad $5.95	ink refill $2.95	stampin' write $3.25	stampin' pad $7.50	ink refill $4.25	8-1/2" x 11" (24 sheets) $5.50	12" x 12" (20 sheets) $7.50	12" x 12" textured	standard cartridge $5.25	jumbo cartridge $7.50
BORDERING BLUE	102265	100940	100070	101374	102530	102630	107092	–	–	–
BROCADE BLUE	101102	100408	100064	101593	100788	101166	107091	–	–	–
BALLET BLUE	100907	101713	100066	102855	101732	100613	106538	–	102305	103662
NIGHT OF NAVY	102977	103033	100069	103181	103131	100867	106547	–	–	103664
TAKEN WITH TEAL	103257	100550	100068	100617	102049	101584	107090	–	–	–
HANDSOME HUNTER	105215	105227	105116	105239	105163	105122	106534	–	105198	105205
ALWAYS ARTICHOKE	105219	105232	105113	105243	105177	105119	107089	–	105199	–
SO SAFFRON	105213	105225	105114	105237	105151	105118	107088	–	105201	–
REGAL ROSE	105211	105223	105108	105235	105149	105130	107087	–	–	–
ROSE RED	101778	102109	100063	101545	102915	102544	107086	–	–	–
BRAVO BURGUNDY	105214	105226	105109	105238	105162	105123	106533	–	105197	105207
ELEGANT EGGPLANT	105210	105222	105110	105234	105148	105126	107085	–	–	–

assorted

	Classic		markers	Craft		card stock			stampin' spots Classic	Craft
	(set of 12) $57.95	(set of 12) $28.95	(set of 12) $31.95	(set of 12) $80.95	(set of 12) $45.95	36 sheets (3 ea. of 12 colors) $7.95	24 sheets (2 ea. of 12 colors) $8.95	24 sheets (2 ea. of 12 colors) $11.95	(set of 12) $22.50	(set of 12) $25.95
RICH REGALS	105564	105556	105540	105560	105440	105567	106526	108696	105552	105437

soft subtles

	Classic		markers	Craft		card stock			cartridges	
	stampin' pad $5.95	ink refill $2.95	stampin' write $3.25	stampin' pad $7.50	ink refill $4.25	8-1/2" x 11" (24 sheets) $5.50	12" x 12" (20 sheets) $7.50	12" x 12" textured	standard cartridge $5.25	jumbo cartridge $7.50
PERFECT PLUM	101437	102107	100035	102869	100697	101889	107084	–	–	103666
PALE PLUM	102732	101268	100036	103271	102202	101658	107083	–	–	–
PRETTY IN PINK	101301	102295	100045	100857	101127	100459	106546	–	–	103668
BLUSH BLOSSOM	102609	100614	100037	102080	100935	103318	107082	–	–	–
APRICOT APPEAL	105218	105231	105107	105242	105166	105124	107081	–	–	–
BARELY BANANA	101170	100639	100039	101609	101676	102701	106543	–	–	–
CERTAINLY CELERY	105217	105230	105106	105241	105165	105125	107080	–	105194	–
MELLOW MOSS	102774	101771	100038	101054	101967	102898	106548	–	–	103667
SAGE SHADOW	102532	100720	100040	103251	100711	101563	107079	–	–	–
BASHFUL BLUE	105209	105221	105111	105233	105146	105120	106535	–	105204	105206
ALMOST AMETHYST	101723	102580	100043	101211	102282	102158	107078	–	–	–
LAVENDER LACE	101305	100862	100041	103144	101590	101614	107077	–	101812	–

assorted

	Classic		markers	Craft		card stock			stampin' spots Classic	Craft
	(set of 12) $57.95	(set of 12) $28.95	(set of 12) $31.95	(set of 12) $80.95	(set of 12) $45.95	36 sheets (3 ea. of 12 colors) $7.95	24 sheets (2 ea. of 12 colors) $8.95	24 sheets (2 ea. of 12 colors) $11.95	(set of 12) $22.50	(set of 12) $25.95
SOFT SUBTLES	105565	105557	105537	105561	105441	105568	106525	108695	105553	105370

naturals

When you're selecting a color scheme, our neutral palette provides the perfect complement to any color combination. Choose the color you like best, or try our specialty paper to achieve a textured look.

Taste of Textiles

These unique specialty papers coordinate with the Manhattan collection and offer a variety of textured options to your paper crafting. 10 sheets: 2 ea. of 5 types. 12" x 12". (printed Vellum with Not Quite Navy Polka Dots, Coated White Pin Stripe, Black Linen Texture, Bronze Metallic, Printed Kraft, Close to Cocoa Pin Stripe)

| 113991 | Taste of Textiles | $9.95 |

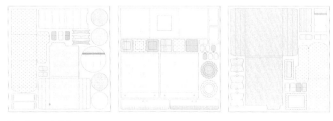

Pockets & Pieces

Close to Cocoa designs printed on Kraft card stock offer monochromatic and versatile die cuts. 2 sheets ea. of 3 designs. 12" x 12".

| 110730 | Office Accents | $8.95 |

Watercolor Paper

100% cotton, cold-pressed 140 lb. watercolor paper. Sized perfectly to layer on your card front. 3-3/4" x 5".

| 105019 | Watercolor Paper (20) | $6.95 |

Card Stock 12" x 12" *sm*

106529	Whisper White (20) *a,l,b*	$7.50
106530	Very Vanilla (20) *a,l,b*	$7.50
107070	Kraft (20) *a,l,b*	$7.50
108590	Naturals Assortment *a,l,b*	$8.95
	20 sheets (4 ea. of 5 colors): Kraft, Naturals White, Naturals Ivory, Confetti White, and Confetti Cream	

Card Stock 8-1/2" x 11"

100730	Whisper White (40) *a,l,b* *sm*	$7.50
101650	Very Vanilla (40) *a,l,b* *sm*	$7.50
102125	Kraft (40) *a,l,b* *sm*	$7.50
102316	Naturals White (40) *a,l,b* *sm*	$7.50
102028	Confetti White (40) *a,l,b* *sm*	$9.50
101910	Shimmery White (10)	$7.95
101849	Naturals Ivory (40) *a,l,b* *sm*	$7.50
102835	Confetti Cream (40) *a,l,b* *sm*	$9.50
102599	Glossy White (25)	$5.95
102935	Brushed Gold (10) *a*	$7.95
100712	Brushed Silver (10) *a*	$7.95

White Vellum *sm*

| 101856 | 8-1/2" x 11" Card Stock (20) *a* | $6.50 |
| 101839 | 8-1/2" x 11" Paper (20) *a* | $4.95 |

a = ACID FREE   l = LIGNIN FREE   b = BUFFERED

bags & calendars

Birthday Calendar

Keep track of birthdays and other important occasions with these perpetual date trackers. Acid free, lignin free, and buffered. 5-1/2" × 14". *sm*

101398	Whisper White	$7.95

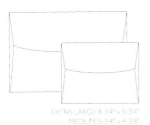

Days-To-Remember Calendar

Scrapbook pages you create enliven each month. The perforated pages can be removed from the calendar and added to an album. Acid free, lignin free, and buffered. Whisper White. *sm*

104144	6" × 6" Desktop Calendar	$9.95

Cellophane Bags

50 per pkg.

103104	Small Flat (3" × 5")	$3.95
102757	Medium Flat (4" × 6")	$4.50
102210	Large Flat (6" × 8")	$4.95

Gift Sacks

3 per pkg. 4-3/4" × 8" × 10-1/2".

100900	White	$2.95

cards & envelopes

Rectangular Envelopes

All of our exclusive envelopes feature a rounded flap for an elegant signature look.

Extra Large Envelopes

107288	Whisper White (20)	$5.50

Medium Envelopes

107301	Whisper White (40)	$6.50
107300	Very Vanilla (40)	$6.50
107297	Kraft (40)	$6.50
107302	Naturals Ivory (40)	$6.50
107303	Naturals White (40)	$6.50
102619	Clear Translucent (50)	$4.95
	(May require extra postage; square flap)	

EXTRA LARGE: 8-3/4" × 5-3/4"
MEDIUM: 5-3/4" × 4-3/8"

Square Envelopes

Medium Square Envelopes

107289	Medium Whisper White (20)	$6.50
	(May require extra postage)	

Mini Square Envelopes

107309	Whisper White (40)	$7.50
	(U.S. Postal Service will not process or deliver)	

MEDIUM: 5-1/2" × 5-1/2"
MINI: 3-1/8" × 3-1/8"

Open-End Envelopes

Small Open-End Envelopes

107286	Whisper White (20)	$7.50

SMALL: 6-3/4" × 3-1/2"

Notes & Envelopes

Precut and scored note cards available in an assortment of our colors.

CARD: 5" × 3-1/2"
ENVELOPE: 5-1/8" × 3-5/8"

Note Cards

Classic note cards include 20 ea. Whisper White cards and envelopes.

107311	Note Cards	$5.95
	Whisper White	

CARD: 4" × 2-11/16"
ENVELOPE: 4-1/4" × 3"

Gift Notes

Interior slot holds gift card securely. 30 cards: 10 of each color. Includes 30 Whisper White envelopes.

111337	Gift Notes II	$9.95
	Kiwi Kiss, Riding Hood Red, Kraft	
	(U.S. Postal Service will not process or deliver)	

CARD: 3" × 3"
ENVELOPE: 3-1/8" × 3-1/8"

Textured Love Notes

30 textured cards: 10 of each color. Includes 30 Very Vanilla envelopes.

111338	Love Notes II	$12.95
	Tangerine Tango, Bashful Blue, Old Olive	
	(U.S. Postal Service will not process or deliver)	

CARD: 4" × 2-3/4"
ENVELOPE: 4-1/4" × 3"

Scallop Notes

The scallop edge on these notes make them an excellent choice for instantly elegant cards. 30 cards: 10 of each color. Includes 30 Very Vanilla envelopes.

111336	Scallop Notes II	$11.95
	Pink Pirouette, Baja Breeze, Chocolate Chip	
	(U.S. Postal Service will not process or deliver)	

CARD: 4" × 4"
ENVELOPE: 4-1/4" × 4-1/4"

Fresh-Cut Notes

Fresh-Cut Notes coordinate with the Fresh Cuts set (page 92) and the 5-Petal Flower punch (page 184). Includes 15 ea. Whisper White envelopes.

111882	Fresh-Cut Notes	$8.95
	Whisper White	
	(U.S. Postal Service will not process or deliver)	

Carousel Notes

Die-cut, scalloped circles coordinate with the Pick a Petal Classy Brass (page 186). 12 cards: 4 in ea. color. Includes 12 Chocolate Chip envelopes.

112139	Carousel Notes II	$11.95
	Ruby Red, Kiwi Kiss, Baja Breeze	
	(Requires extra postage)	

CARD: 3-7/8" × 5-7/8"
ENVELOPE: 6-1/8" × 6-1/8"

designer series paper

Our 12" × 12" Designer Series paper features exclusive patterns printed on both sides. The coordinating card stock colors are listed below each paper assortment. All sheets can be trimmed to create 6" × 6" and 8-1/2" × 11" pages. 12 sheets: 2 ea. of 6 double-sided designs. Acid and lignin free. *sm*

The Parisian Breeze, Sweet Slumber, and To the Nines specialty Designer Series papers are printed on textured, cover-weight card stock. Rockabilly has a printed gloss design.

114039 Rockabilly Specialty (Printed gloss design) $11.95
Basic Black, Riding Hood Red, Kiwi Kiss

113993 Parisian Breeze Specialty (Textured, cover-weight card stock) $11.95
Baja Breeze, Chocolate Chip, Kraft

114038 To the Nines Specialty (Textured, cover-weight card stock) $11.95
Sahara Sand, Sage Shadow, Always Artichoke, Chocolate Chip

114037 Sweet Slumber Specialty (Textured, cover-weight card stock) $11.95
Ruby Red, Baja Breeze, So Saffron, Sahara Sand

ALL PAPER PATTERN SWATCHES SHOWN AT 25%

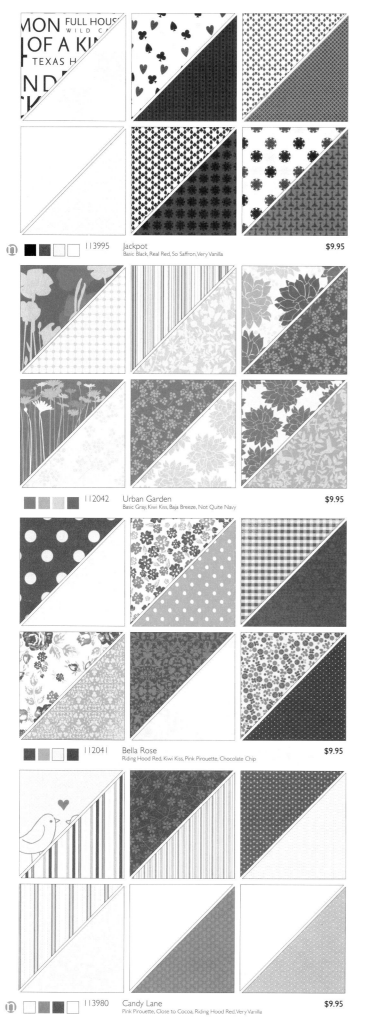

113995 Jackpot $9.95
Basic Black, Real Red, So Saffron, Very Vanilla

112042 Urban Garden $9.95
Basic Gray, Kiwi Kiss, Baja Breeze, Not Quite Navy

112041 Bella Rose $9.95
Riding Hood Red, Kiwi Kiss, Pink Pirouette, Chocolate Chip

113980 Candy Lane $9.95
Pink Pirouette, Close to Cocoa, Riding Hood Red, Very Vanilla

Patterns Designer Series Papers

Available in 14 of our most popular colors, this paper offers a design for every project.
12 sheets: 2 ea. of 6 double-sided designs. *sm*

	112164	Chocolate Chip	$9.95
	112156	Pink Pirouette	$9.95
	112162	Rose Red	$9.95
	112155	Riding Hood Red	$9.95
	112159	Pumpkin Pie	$9.95
	112158	Perfect Plum	$9.95
	112150	Pacific Point	$9.95
	112151	Bashful Blue	$9.95
	112157	Baja Breeze	$9.95
	112160	Old Olive	$9.95
	112154	Certainly Celery	$9.95
	112161	Kiwi Kiss	$9.95
	112152	So Saffron	$9.95
	112153	Tangerine Tango	$9.95

SHOWN IN PERFECT PLUM

159

113981   Bella Birds $9.95
Chocolate Chip, Bordering Blue, So Saffron, Pink Pirouette

113976   Pink Flamingo $9.95
Chocolate Chip, Real Red, Summer Sun, Cameo Coral, Tempting Turquoise

112464   Manchester $9.95
Baja Breeze, Always Artichoke, Kraft, Very Vanilla

113966   Good Morning Sunshine $9.95
Pacific Point, Kiwi Kiss, Summer Sun, Chocolate Chip

112471   Rainbow Sherbet $9.95
Tempting Turquoise, Green Galore, Apricot Appeal, Gable Green

113975   Raspberry Tart $9.95
Real Red, Rose Red, Cameo Coral, Pretty in Pink, Kiwi Kiss

160   © 1990–2009 STAMPIN' UP!

ALL PAPER PATTERN SWATCHES SHOWN AT 25%

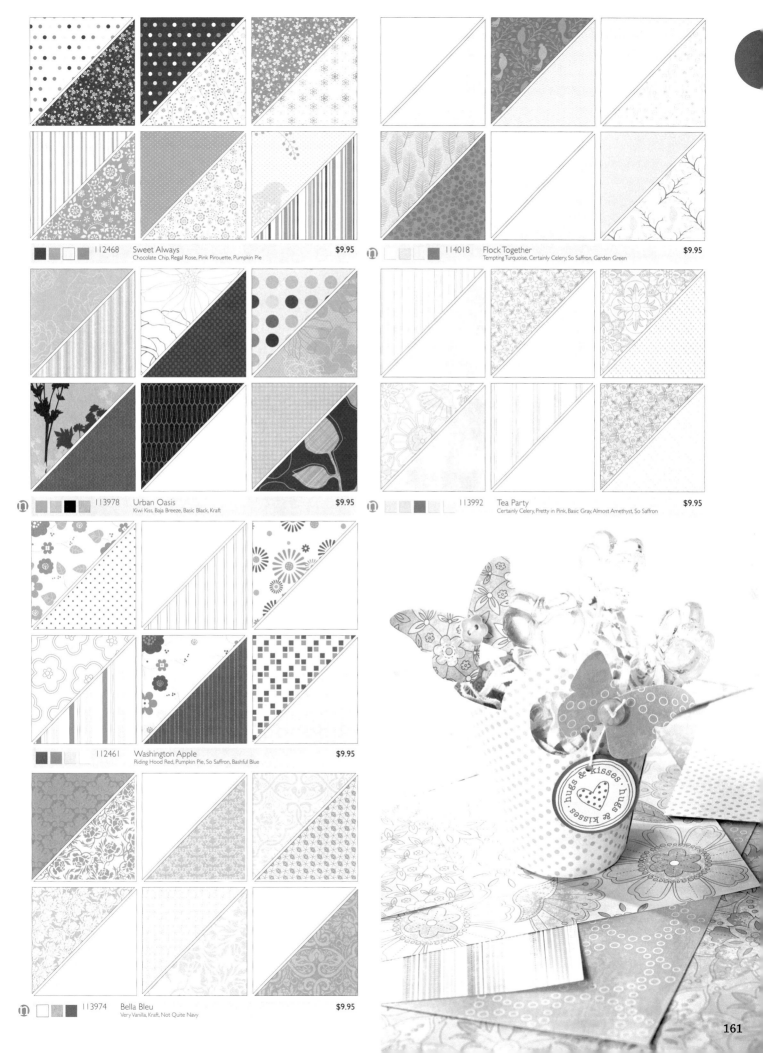

	112468	Sweet Always	$9.95

Chocolate Chip, Regal Rose, Pink Pirouette, Pumpkin Pie

	114018	Flock Together	$9.95

Tempting Turquoise, Certainly Celery, So Saffron, Garden Green

	113978	Urban Oasis	$9.95

Kiwi Kiss, Baja Breeze, Basic Black, Kraft

	113992	Tea Party	$9.95

Certainly Celery, Pretty in Pink, Basic Gray, Almost Amethyst, So Saffron

	112461	Washington Apple	$9.95

Riding Hood Red, Pumpkin Pie, So Saffron, Bashful Blue

	113974	Bella Bleu	$9.95

Very Vanilla, Kraft, Not Quite Navy

simply scrappin'

Preserve your photos with our coordinated Simply Scrappin' kits, complete with self-adhesive die cuts, patterned paper, and card stock. Trim sheets with the Paper Cutter (page 189) to create 6" x 6" and 8-1/2" x 11" pages. *sm*

Create coordinating pages with our Simply Scrappin'. Each one includes coordinating card stock, Designer Series paper, and self-adhesive die cuts, so your scrapbook pages will come together simply and beautifully.

113059   Petal Party $19.95

3 SHEETS EA. 12" x 12" DOUBLE-SIDED PAPER

 OLD OLIVE
 SO SAFFRON
 PUMPKIN PIE
 PIXIE PINK

2 SHEETS EA. 12" x 12" TEXTURED CARD STOCK

The coordinating Best Wishes & More set and sample made from this kit are shown on page 55.

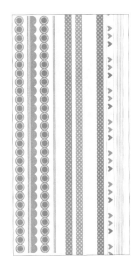

2 SHEETS EA. 6" x 12" SELF-ADHESIVE DIE CUTS

112054   Best Ever $19.95

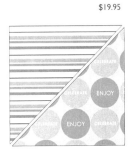

3 SHEETS EA. 12" x 12" DOUBLE-SIDED PAPER

 RIDING HOOD RED
 WHISPER WHITE
 BAJA BREEZE
 KIWI KISS

2 SHEETS EA. 12" x 12" TEXTURED CARD STOCK

The coordinating Big Bold Birthday set is shown on page 40.

(ESP) 112970   Lo Mejor de Todo

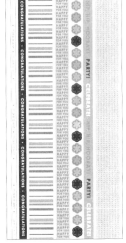

2 SHEETS EA. 6" x 12" SELF-ADHESIVE DIE CUTS

ALL PAPER PATTERN SWATCHES SHOWN AT 25%

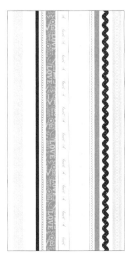

2 SHEETS EA. 6" × 12" SELF-ADHESIVE DIE CUTS

113918   Love Sparkles $19.95

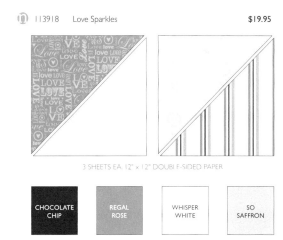

3 SHEETS EA. 12" × 12" DOUBLE-SIDED PAPER

| CHOCOLATE CHIP | REGAL ROSE | WHISPER WHITE | SO SAFFRON |

2 SHEETS EA. 12" × 12" TEXTURED CARD STOCK

The coordinating A Happy Heart set is shown on page 26.

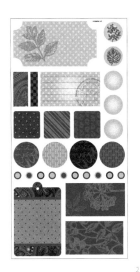

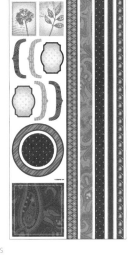

2 SHEETS EA. 6" × 12" SELF-ADHESIVE DIE CUTS

114326   Tailor Made $19.95

3 SHEETS EA. 12" × 12" DOUBLE-SIDED PAPER

| NOT QUITE NAVY | ALWAYS ARTICHOKE | CHOCOLATE CHIP | SAHARA SAND |

2 SHEETS EA. 12" × 12" TEXTURED CARD STOCK

The coordinating Lexicon of Leaves and Le Jardin Botanique sets are shown on page 101.

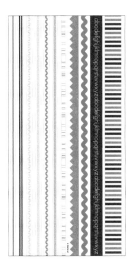

2 SHEETS EA. 6" × 12" SELF-ADHESIVE DIE CUTS

113936   Hoppy Memories $19.95

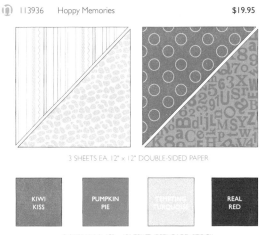

3 SHEETS EA. 12" × 12" DOUBLE-SIDED PAPER

| KIWI KISS | PUMPKIN PIE | TEMPTING TURQUOISE | REAL RED |

2 SHEETS EA. 12" × 12" TEXTURED CARD STOCK

The coordinating ABC Alphabet set is shown on page 146.

113925   Sweet Nothings $19.95

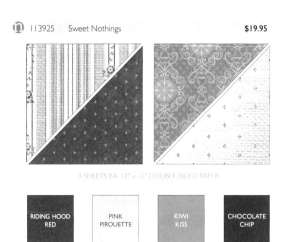

3 SHEETS EA. 12" × 12" DOUBLE-SIDED PAPER

| RIDING HOOD RED | PINK PIROUETTE | KIWI KISS | CHOCOLATE CHIP |

2 SHEETS EA. 12" × 12" TEXTURED CARD STOCK

The coordinating Freinds 24-7 set is shown on page 81.

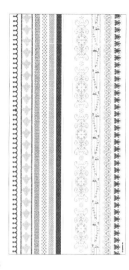

2 SHEETS EA. 6" × 12" SELF-ADHESIVE DIE-CUTS

113911   Sunshine Garden $19.95

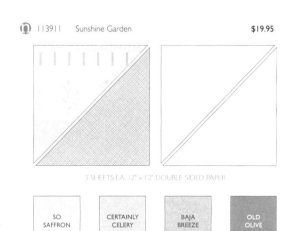

3 SHEETS EA. 12" × 12" DOUBLE-SIDED PAPER

| SO SAFFRON | CERTAINLY CELERY | BAJA BREEZE | OLD OLIVE |

2 SHEETS EA. 12" × 12" TEXTURED CARD STOCK

2 SHEETS EA. 6" × 12" SELF-ADHESIVE DIE-CUTS

112179   Love Stories $19.95

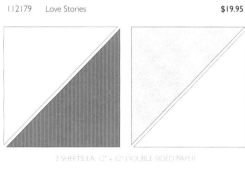

3 SHEETS EA. 12" × 12" DOUBLE-SIDED PAPER

| PINK PIROUETTE | CERTAINLY CELERY | BASHFUL BLUE | CLOSE TO COCOA |

2 SHEETS EA. 12" × 12" TEXTURED CARD STOCK

The coordinating Together Forever is shown on page 60.

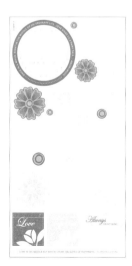

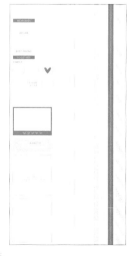

2 SHEETS EA. 6" × 12" SELF-ADHESIVE DIE-CUTS

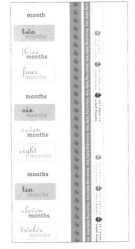

2 SHEETS EA. 6" × 12" SELF-ADHESIVE DIE CUTS

112172   Rock-a-Bye Boy $19.95

3 SHEETS EA. 12" × 12" DOUBLE-SIDED PAPER

CHOCOLATE CHIP   BASHFUL BLUE   OLD OLIVE   TANGERINE TANGO

2 SHEETS EA. 12" × 12" TEXTURED CARD STOCK

The coordinating Nursery Necessities set is shown on page 66.

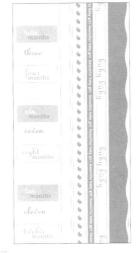

2 SHEETS EA. 6" × 12" SELF-ADHESIVE DIE CUTS

112165   Rock-a-Bye Girl $19.95

3 SHEETS EA. 12" × 12" DOUBLE-SIDED PAPER

REGAL ROSE   BASHFUL BLUE   KIWI KISS   PINK PIROUETTE

2 SHEETS EA. 12" × 12" TEXTURED CARD STOCK

The coordinating Nursery Necessities set is shown on page 66.

2 SHEETS EA. 6" × 12" SELF-ADHESIVE DIE CUTS

113943   2 Sweet $19.95

3 SHEETS EA. 12" × 12" DOUBLE-SIDED PAPER

BASIC GRAY   PERFECT PLUM   PALE PLUM   KIWI KISS

2 SHEETS EA. 12" × 12" TEXTURED CARD STOCK

The coordinating Jumbo Outline Alphabet set is shown on page 144.

simply sent card elements

Our Simply Sent Card Elements include the components you need to embellish and create fun, vibrant cards.
Photos and project instructions are included. Each kit creates nine 4-1/4" x 5-1/2" cards (3 ea. in 3 styles).
Coordinating stamp sets (sold separately) are shown by each kit. Envelopes are sold separately on page 157.

| 112021 | Rock Star Card Elements | $15.95 |
| 111696 | Starring You (stamp set of 4) | $13.95 |

Included Accessories

4 feet of Old Olive 5/8" Grosgrain Ribbon
5 feet of More Mustard 1/4" Grosgrain Ribbon
3 large More Mustard Buttons
(Stamp set, adhesive, and ink not included)

BASHFUL BLUE | OLD OLIVE | MORE MUSTARD

2 SHEETS EA. 8-1/2" x 11" TEXTURED CARD STOCK

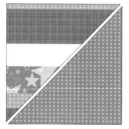

2 SHEETS 8-1/2" x 11" DOUBLE-SIDED PAPER

1 SHEET 8-1/2" x 11" SELF-ADHESIVE DIE CUTS

CELEBRATE TODAY

way to go

HAPPY HAPPY HAPPY HAPPY birthday HAPPY HAPPY HAPPY HAPPY

set of **4** | **Starring You**
111696 $13.95

 ESP 112949 Celebremos

ESP 112962 Elementos para tarjetas estrella de rock Simply Sent

© 1990–2009 STAMPIN' UP!

ALL PAPER PATTERN SWATCHES SHOWN AT 25%

112028	Flower Power Card Elements	$15.95
111714	Wow Flowers (stamp set of 4)	$12.95

Included Accessories

5 feet of Whisper White 1/4" Grosgrain Ribbon
3-1/2 feet of More Mustard 1/4" Grosgrain Ribbon
3 large More Mustard Buttons
3 small Old Olive Buttons
5 More Mustard Brads
(Stamp set, adhesive, and ink not included)

ROSE RED   OLD OLIVE   PERFECT PLUM

2 SHEETS EA. 8-1/2" × 11" TEXTURED CARD STOCK

1 SHEET 8-1/2" × 11" SELF-ADHESIVE DIE CUTS

2 SHEETS 8-1/2" × 11" DOUBLE-SIDED PAPER

birthday wishes

THANK YOU

ESP 112955 **Flores llamativas**

Wow Flowers | *set of* **4**
111714 $12.95

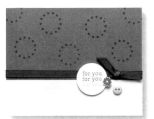

114572	Thankful Thinking Card Elements	$15.95
113786	Thankful Thinking (stamp set of 6)	$13.95

Included Accessories

4 feet of Chocolate Chip 5/8" Grosgrain Ribbon
5-1/2 feet of Chocolate Chip 1/4" Grosgrain Ribbon
3 Styled Silver Brads
3 small Bashful Blue Buttons
3 small Very Vanilla Buttons
(Stamp set, adhesive, and ink not included)

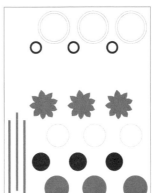

RUBY RED   KRAFT   BASHFUL BLUE

2 SHEETS EA. 8-1/2" × 11" CARD STOCK

1 SHEET 8-1/2" × 11" SELF-ADHESIVE DIE CUTS

2 SHEETS 8-1/2" × 11" SINGLE-SIDED PAPER

thanks
for you
THINKING OF YOU

Thankful Thinking | *set of* **6**
113786 $13.95

ESP 114020 Pensamientos de Agradecimiento

simply sent card elements & more

Put cards together quickly with our Simply Sent Card Elements & More, which include the items you need—
including stamp set and ink—to create fun cards. Easy-to-use project instructions will help you make 8 cards and
coordinating envelopes. Contents are packaged in a reusable Craft Keeper. (Adhesive not included.)

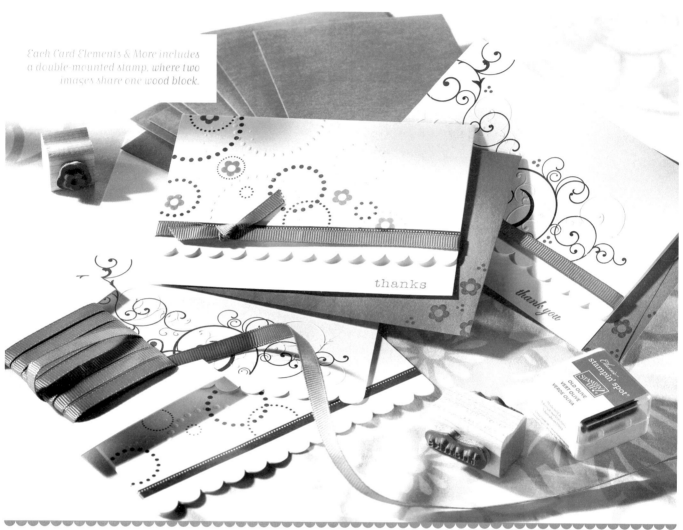

*Each Card Elements & More includes
a double-mounted stamp, where two
images share one wood block.*

	114594	Thanks x 2 Card Elements & More	$24.95
		Chocolate Chip, Old Olive	

Included Accessories

Old Olive Classic Stampin' Spot®
11 feet Old Olive 1/4" Grosgrain Ribbon
Thanks x 2 *(double-mounted stamp set of 4)*

8 OLD OLIVE 5-1/8" x 3-5/8" ENVELOPES

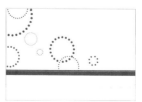

8 PRINTED, DIE-CUT, AND EMBOSSED CARDS (2 DESIGNS, 4 OF EA.)

8 CHOCOLATE CHIP CAROUSEL NOTES

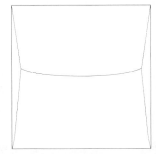

8 CHOCOLATE CHIP 6-1/8" x 6-1/8" ENVELOPES

114579   2U Card Elements & More   **$24.95**
Chocolate Chip, Very Vanilla, Tempting Turquoise
(May require extra postage)

Included Accessories

Ruby Red Classic Stampin' Spot
2 yards Riding Hood Red 1-1/4" Striped Grosgrain Ribbon
2U (double-mounted stamp set of 2)

8 TEMPTING TURQUOISE PRE-GLITTERED CHIPBOARD

8 CHOCOLATE CHIP LAMINATE CHIPBOARD

HAPPY
birthday   thanks

8 TEMPTING TURQUOISE CARD STOCK DIE CUTS

16 VERY VANILLA CARD STOCK DIE CUTS

8 CHIPBOARD FLOWERS

8 WHISPER WHITE 5-3/4" x 4-3/8" ENVELOPES

114585   It's about You Card Elements & More   **$24.95**
Bashful Blue, Pumpkin Pie, So Saffron, Garden Green
(May require extra postage)

Included Accessories

Garden Green Classic Stampin' Spot
5/16" Chocolate Chip Brads (8)
10 feet of 5/8" twill tape
It's about You (double-mounted stamp set of 2)

SO VERY **HAPPY** FOR **YOU**!

YOU ARE **IN** MY **THOUGHTS**

1 SHEET 6" x 8-1/2" SELF-ADHESIVE DIE CUTS

BASHFUL BLUE   GARDEN GREEN   PUMPKIN PIE

ASSORTED CARD STOCK PIECES

8 PIECES 4-1/4" x 5-1/2" SINGLE-SIDED PAPER

169

simply sent card kits

Take the guesswork out of card making. Just follow our simple project instructions and photos to make cards suitable for many occasions. Use our Card Kits to create two styles of cards in one sitting. A coordinating stamp set is included.

 109231   Sending Happy Thoughts $54.95
Old Olive, Pumpkin Pie, Real Red, Very Vanilla

Sending Happy Thoughts Simply Sent Kit Includes:

Sending Happy Thoughts (stamp set of 6)
Old Olive Classic Stampin' Spot
Pumpkin Pie Classic Stampin' Spot
Real Red Classic Stampin' Spot
Zig Zag Twill Tape
Pewter Brads
2-Way Glue Pen
Dazzling Diamonds Stampin' Glitter
Stampin' Dimensionals
Mini Glue Dots®
Card Stock Assortment
12 Very Vanilla Envelopes

Kit creates 10 cards (5 ea. in 2 styles)
Card size: 4-1/4" x 5-1/2"

sending happy thoughts

| | 114598 | No One Like You | $42.95 |

114598   No One Like You $42.95
Bashful Blue, Kraft, Chocolate Chip, Very Vanilla

No One Like You Simply Sent Kit Includes:

No One Like You (stamp set of 5)
VersaMark Cube
Bashful Blue Classic Stampin' Spot
Chocolate Chip Classic Stampin' Spot
Chocolate Chip 1/4" Grosgrain Ribbon
Kraft 3/8" Taffeta Ribbon
Pewter Vintage Brads
Small Bashful Blue Buttons
Card Stock, Textured Card Stock & Designer Series Paper Assortment
Stampin' Dimensionals
Mini Glue Dots
12 Small Open-End Kraft Envelopes

Kit creates 10 cards (5 ea. in 2 styles)
Card size: 3" x 6"

THERE IS NO
ONE LIKE YOU

thinking
OF YOU

114605   More Thoughts $42.95
Rose Red, Always Artichoke, Pretty in Pink

More Thoughts Simply Sent Kit Includes:

More Thoughts (stamp set of 4)
Rose Red Classic Stampin' Spot
Always Artichoke Classic Stampin' Spot
Pretty in Pink Classic Stampin' Spot
On Board Chipboard pieces
Self-Adhesive Die Cuts
Stampin' Dimensionals
Mini Glue Dots
14 Whisper White Envelopes
Card Stock Assortment

Kit creates 12 cards (6 ea. in 2 styles)
Card size: 4-1/4" x 5-1/2"

thanks

thinking
OF YOU

happy
BIRTHDAY

171

rub-ons

Our Rub-Ons are easy to apply and enhance any card stock, patterned paper, or stamped image. The eye-catching images are designed to complement many of our stamp sets, so your creations will be easy to coordinate. Use Rub-Ons on paper and most nonporous surfaces. Bright Delights Rub-Ons include 2 sheets that feature 4 colors. All other Rub-Ons include 1 sheet ea. in colors noted by each design. 5-7/8" × 12".

113887   Bright Delights $11.95
Rose Red, Tangerine Tango, Kiwi Kiss, Chocolate Chip

113884   Fashion District $10.95
Whisper White, Chocolate Chip

111416   Chateau Bella $10.95
Whisper White, Chocolate Chip

111414   Hidden Garden* $10.95
Whisper White, Chocolate Chip

| | 111415 | Greatest Moments | $10.95 |
Whisper White, Chocolate Chip

| | 113889 | Laughter and Love | $10.95 |
Whisper White, Chocolate Chip

| | 113888 | Many Occasions | $10.95 |
Whisper White, Chocolate Chip

| | 113886 | Planter Box | $10.95 |
Whisper White, Chocolate Chip

| | 111804 | Chit Chat | $10.95 |
Whisper White, Chocolate Chip

| | 111277 | A Perfect Day | $10.95 |
Whisper White, Basic Black

embellishments

Eyelets, brads, Hodgepodge Hardware, and more—we've got the embellishments you need to adorn your handcrafted creations. The variety of colors and assortments available makes it easy to mix and match.

Rhinestone Brads

Add a bit of sparkle to any project! Each circle assortment includes approx. 80 brads; 4 colors, 3 sizes. Each square assortment includes approx. 80 brads; 4 colors, 2 sizes. Clear assortment includes approx. 84 brads; 28 ea. of 3 sizes. Small shown below.

113144	Clear (84)	$10.95
109110	Circle Fire Pink, Red, Pumpkin, Yellow	$10.95
109111	Circle Ice Lilac, Light Blue, Turquoise, Green	$10.95
109112	Square Fire Pink, Red, Pumpkin, Yellow	$10.95
109113	Square Ice Lilac, Light Blue, Turquoise, Green	$10.95

Jumbo Brads

Our jumbo brads come in 2 sizes that are sure to suit your projects! 5/16" Neutrals assortment includes approx. 80 brads; 20 ea. of 4 colors listed below. 5/8" Neutrals assortment includes approx. 32 brads; 8 ea. of 4 colors listed below.

112534	5/16" Neutrals Assortment Chocolate Chip, Very Vanilla, Whisper White, Silver	$7.95
112533	5/8" Neutrals Assortment Chocolate Chip, Very Vanilla, Whisper White, Silver	$6.95

Build-A-Brad

Punch a 1/2" circle of Designer Series paper or stamp a custom image to build your own brad! Kit includes 24 ea. brad bases and adhesive acrylic bubbles.

109108	Antique Brass	$9.95
109128	Pewter	$9.95

Brads

Exclusive colors coordinate beautifully with many of our other accessories. Approx. 200 per container. Assortments include approx. 50 ea. of 4 colors.

104337	Gold	$6.95
104336	Silver	$6.95
109109	Vintage Black, Silver, Antique Brass, Pewter	$8.95
106957	Bold Brights Brilliant Blue, Green Galore, Real Red, Tempting Turquoise	$8.95
106955	Earth Elements More Mustard, Old Olive, Not Quite Navy, Ruby Red	$8.95
106953	Rich Regals Always Artichoke, Brocade Blue, Rose Red, So Saffron	$8.95
106954	Soft Subtles Apricot Appeal, Bashful Blue, Certainly Celery, Pretty in Pink	$8.95

Eyelets

Eyelet tools sold separately. Assortment includes approx. 50 ea. of 4 colors.

105319	Metallic Gold, Silver, Copper, Antique Brass	$5.95

Jumbo Eyelets

Work beautifully with the Crop-A-Dile. Use with On Board chipboard to make perfect rivets for altered/custom books! Approx. 60 eyelets.

ANTIQUE BRASS   PEWTER

108431	Antique Brass	$9.95
108432	Pewter	$9.95

                    EMBELLISHMENTS ON THIS PAGE SHOWN AT ACTUAL SIZE

Designer Brads

High-quality, cast brads come in custom Stampin' Up! designs, shapes, and Styled Silver finish. Use separately or with our Hodgepodge Hardware. Unless otherwise noted, each assortment includes 16 pieces: 8 ea. of 2 sizes.

112579	Flower (16)	$5.95
112577	Filigree (16; also includes 16 3/16" brads)	$5.95
112571	Circle (16)	$5.95
112572	Star (16)	$5.95
112583	Flower Assortment (32 1/2" brads: 8 ea. of 4 colors)	$6.95

Pumpkin Pie, Pretty in Pink, So Saffron, Chocolate Chip

FLOWER   CIRCLE

FILIGREE   STAR   FLOWER ASSORTMENT

EMBELLISHMENTS ABOVE SHOWN AT 75%

Designer Hardware**

Custom designed to coordinate with our Manhattan and Retro Fresh collections, these large, painted eyelets add whimsy and fun to your creations. 6 pieces per pkg.

114350	Soho	$4.95
	Baja Breeze, Kiwi Kiss	
114351	Hooray	$4.95
	Rose Red, Kiwi Kiss, Summer Sun, Pacific Point	

SOHO   HOORAY

A SELECTION OF THE BELOW PIECES IS INCLUDED.
PIECES ARE SHOWN AT 50% OF ACTUAL SIZE.

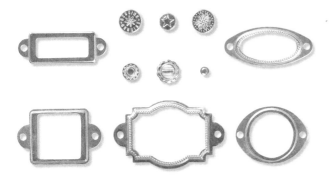

SHOWN AT ACTUAL SIZE

STYLED SILVER   STYLED VANILLA

Hodgepodge Hardware

Our Hodgepodge Hardware includes fresh designs in two finishes. These high quality metal accents coordinate with many of our punches. Kit contents: Raised Dots Designer holders (10); Small Rectangle holders (10); Raised Dots Designer holders (10); 1" Circle holders (10); Square holders (10); 1/2" Genuine brads (10); 3/8" Star brads (10); 1/2" Flower Brads (10); 3/8" Flower brads (10); Flower ribbon slides (10); 3/16" Brads (100).

111325	Styled Silver*	$29.95
112454	Styled Vanilla*	$29.95

A SELECTION OF THE BELOW PIECES IS INCLUDED.
PIECES ARE SHOWN AT 50% OF ACTUAL SIZE.

Pretties Kit

Use this versatile kit to embellish all of your works of heart! Use Stampin' Pastels, Watercolor Wonder Crayons, or Classic ink to dye the flowers to coordinate with our exclusive colors. Kit contents: White flowers (50: 10 ea. in 5 sizes); White halfback pearls (30 small, 20 medium, 10 large); Cream halfback pearls (30 small, 20 medium, 10 large); White round pearls w/ holes (30 small, 15 large); Cream round pearls w/ holes (30 small, 15 large); Clear round beads w/ center hole (10); Clear round beads w/ side hole (10), Clear teardrops (20), Clear round rhinestone brads (20 small, 15 medium, 15 large); Hat Pins w/ clutches (10); Spacer beads (30).

109114	Pretties Kit*	$29.95

buttons & clips

Accessories are the icing on the cake, and now you can step up all
your projects with more buttons and clips than ever before.

Colored Buttons

Hand-dyed to coordinate with a selection of our exclusive colors. Approx. 80 square and circle buttons in 2 sizes.

107421	Fresh Favorites I		$6.95
	Apricot Appeal, Certainly Celery, Not Quite Navy, Tempting Turquoise		
107422	Fresh Favorites II		$6.95
	Always Artichoke, Brocade Blue, Rose Red, So Saffron		

Corduroy Buttons

Add texture to your projects using these custom colored buttons and beads. 24 pieces, 8 ea. of buttons shown.

114338	Kiwi Kiss	$9.95
114339	Chocolate Chip	$9.95
114340	Kraft	$9.95
114341	Pacific Point	$9.95
114342	Pumpkin Pie	$9.95
114343	Summer Sun	$9.95

Designer Buttons

Includes 30 buttons, 3 ea. of button shown.

112092	Button Bouquet	$7.95
	Pink Pirouette, Riding Hood Red, Baja Breeze, Kiwi Kiss	
114333	Button Latte	$7.95
	Chocolate Chip, So Saffron, Very Vanilla, Whisper White	

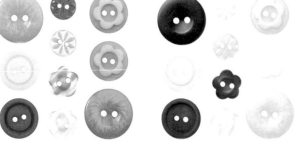

Clear Buttons

Dress up these buttons by applying Rub-On images or by stamping and attaching a cut-out shape to the button. 8 ea. in three sizes: 3/4" circle, 1" circle, and 1" square.

105447	Clear Buttons		$4.95

Clips Assortment

These exclusive clips give your projects the right touch. Assortment includes 24 pieces in our Styled Silver finish. 8 ea. 1/2" × 3/4" Wide clip, 2" small binder clip, and 1/2" × 3/4" Wide clip.

112580	Clips Assortment		$6.95

1/2" Library Clips

Our custom colored library clips in a new size. Assortment includes approx. 24 pieces, 8 ea. of 3 colors (Chocolate Chip, Old Olive, and Whisper White).

112581	1/2" Library Clips		$6.95

Mini Library Clips

Innovative library clips are available in 12 ea. of 4 colors (Black, Silver, Antique Brass, and Pewter). Clip size 1/4" × 1/2".

109857	Mini Library Clips		$12.95

Metal Edge Tags

These fun tags are great to stamp on, or customize using vellum or Designer Series paper. Each package contains six 2" tags and six 1 1/2" tags. Shown at 40%.

103374	Aluminum White Circle		$4.25

accents & elements

Use our exclusive Accents & Elements to create unforgettable embellishments for all your crafting projects.
Each piece is die cut for your convenience. Coordinating colors are listed by each item number.

Canvas Cuts

These die-cut, canvas sheets coordinate with our Fashion District Rub-Ons (page 172) and add
subtle dimension and texture to your project. 4 sheets: 2 sheets ea. design. 6" × 6".

113979	Canvas Cuts	$7.95

POSIES SHOWN AT 50%

Fleurettes

Use these handmade, crocheted flowers to add a delicate touch to any project. 12 flowers: 4
ea. of 3 Flowers shown—1", 1.25", and 1.5".

	114019	Fleurettes	$9.95
		Pink Pirouette, Riding Hood Red, Whisper White	

FLOWERS SHOWN AT 50% IN CHOCOLATE CHIP

Flower Fusion

Custom colored felt flowers will add an eclectic dimension to any of your projects. 14 flower
designs in 3 colors. More than 130 individual pieces packaged in a fun tin.

	110720	Flower Fusion	$14.95
		Pumpkin Pie, Rose Red, Old Olive	
	112006	Flower Fusion Too	$14.95
		Pink Pirouette, Baja Breeze, Chocolate Chip	

ribbon

Need a quick accent for your tag, gift, or card? Our ribbon, available on spools in a variety of widths and Stampin' Up! colors, is a choice option. With ribbon this adorable, you'll invent projects just to use it.

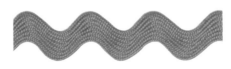

Ribbon Originals
Approx. 9 yds: 3 ea. of 3 designs.

	114317	Dress Up	$12.95

So Saffron, Whisper White, Riding Hood Red

Ribbon Originals
Approx. 10 yds: 5 ea. of 2 designs.

	114316	Pig Tails	$13.95

Kiwi Kiss, Pumpkin Pie

Ribbon Originals
Approx. 9 yds: 3 ea. of 3 designs.

	114318	Valet	$12.95

Baja Breeze, Chocolate Chip, Basic Black

1" Double-Stitched Grosgrain Ribbon
Grosgrain ribbon features a double-stitched pattern; use alone or layer it with other ribbon. 1" wide, approx. 10 yds.

	111846	Rose Red	$8.95
	111847	Baja Breeze	$8.95
	111848	Bashful Blue	$8.95
	111849	Chocolate Chip	$8.95

1/2" Striped Grosgrain Ribbon
Enjoy our classic grosgrain ribbon, available in this striped pattern. 1/2" wide, approx. 10 yds.

	110717	Bashful Blue	$7.95
	110715	Pumpkin Pie	$7.95
	110714	Real Red	$7.95
	113883	Old Olive	$7.95
	113882	Pretty in Pink	$7.95
	113699	So Saffron	$7.95

5/8" Striped Grosgrain Ribbon
Embellish your projects with this ribbon, available in our In Colors. 5/8" wide, approx. 15 yds.

	111374	Riding Hood Red	$9.95
	111373	Pink Pirouette	$9.95
	111375	Baja Breeze	$9.95
	111370	Pacific Point	$9.95
	111372	Kiwi Kiss	$9.95
	111371	Tangerine Tango	$9.95

Organza Ribbon

Add graceful delicacy to your projects with this Whisper White organza ribbon. 5/8" wide, approx. 15 yds.

	114319	Whisper White	$5.95

Hemp Twine

Approx. 12 yds.

	101259	Black	$2.95
	100982	Natural	$2.95
	102875	Red	$2.95

Linen Thread

Diameter is fine enough for use with buttons or with needles from our Crafters' Tool Kit. Approx. 15 yds.

	104199	Linen Thread	$4.50

1/4" Grosgrain Ribbon

High-quality exclusive ribbon gives your project the perfect touch. 1/4" wide, approx. 15 yds.

	109027	Basic Black	$4.95
	109025	Whisper White	$4.95
	109026	Very Vanilla	$4.95
	109030	Pumpkin Pie	$4.95
	109040	Apricot Appeal	$4.95
	109032	Pretty in Pink	$4.95
	109034	Real Red	$4.95
	111366	Rose Red	$4.95
	109028	Bravo Burgundy	$4.95
	109039	Elegant Eggplant	$4.95
	109036	Night of Navy	$4.95
	109038	Tempting Turquoise	$4.95
	109029	Bashful Blue	$4.95
	111369	Sage Shadow	$4.95
	109031	Certainly Celery	$4.95
	111368	Old Olive	$4.95
	109033	Mellow Moss	$4.95
	109035	Always Artichoke	$4.95
	111367	Chocolate Chip	$4.95

Gingham Ribbon

Add a touch of nostalgia to your projects. 3/16" wide, approx. 15 yds.

	104832	Black	$7.50
	104827	Red	$7.50

5/8" Grosgrain Ribbon

Wide grosgrain ribbon in many of our popular colors. 5/8" wide, approx. 15 yds.

	109055	Very Vanilla	$7.95
	109051	Chocolate Chip	$7.95
	109053	Bravo Burgundy	$7.95
	109052	Real Red	$7.95
	109056	Regal Rose	$7.95
	109057	Brocade Blue	$7.95
	109050	Certainly Celery	$7.95
	109054	Old Olive	$7.95

 ## Satin Ribbon

Double-sided ribbon features Very Vanilla on one side and Kiwi Kiss on the other. 3/8" wide, approx. 10 yds.

	111879	Kiwi Kiss/Very Vanilla	$7.95

Taffeta Ribbon

Timeless ribbon adds a touch of elegance to any project. 3/8" wide, approx. 10 yds.

	109070	Whisper White	$6.95
	109071	Very Vanilla	$6.95
	109068	Kraft	$6.95
	109065	Chocolate Chip	$6.95
	109064	Basic Gray	$6.95
	109069	Mellow Moss	$6.95
	109066	Bashful Blue	$6.95
	109067	Pretty in Pink	$6.95
	111365	Riding Hood Red (with Very Vanilla trim)	$6.95

1-1/4" Grosgrain Ribbon

This versatile ribbon coordinates with the Sweet Bella line. 1-1/4" wide, approx. 10 yds.

	111363	Pink Pirouette	$7.95

7/8" Poly-Twill Ribbon

Our poly-twill ribbon offers a soft, smooth finish. 7/8" wide, approx. 10 yds.

	111364	So Saffron	$8.95

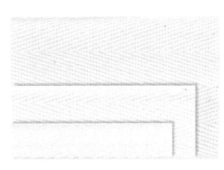

Twill Tape

Use alone, or create a custom look with our stamps or Rub-Ons. 100% cotton twill tape can be dyed with our Classic ink refills. Approx. 9 yds., 3 yds. ea. of 3/8", 3/4", and 1-1/2" tape.

105245	Twill Tape	$5.95

beads & glitter

Twinkle, twinkle, little star . . . Your stars—and projects—are sure to shine with help from our beads and glitter assortments. Just choose the color or palette that coordinates with your project.

Sticky Cuts Sweet

2 sheets of die-cut words and images coordinate with the Retro Fresh line. Use with our Stampin' Glitter or Bead Duo. 12" × 12".

114301	Sticky Cuts Sweet	$8.95

Sticky Cuts Letters

Use with our Duo Beads or Stampin' Glitter to make personalizing your projects, gifts, and work spaces easy and fun. 2 sheets included. 12" × 12".

111109	Sticky Cuts Letters	$8.95

Bead Duo

Monochromatic bead assortments contain approx. 30 grams of colored micro beads and 30 grams of assorted hexagon and bugle beads, each packaged in a Stampin' Store mini container.

110752	Pink Duo (Clear Micro Beads)	$9.95
110753	Blue Duo	$9.95
110754	Green Duo	$9.95
110732	Orange Duo	$9.95
110731	Red Duo	$9.95
110733	Silver Duo	$9.95

Apply larger beads to your project first, and use the coordinating micro beads to fill in the spaces. Use with Sticky Cuts, Sticky Strip, or Tombow Multi Purpose Adhesive.

Sticky Pages

Use sheets to cover On Board albums with Designer Series paper or create your own Sticky Cuts with the Big Shot. These are only two of the possibilities with these sticky sheets! See what you can create. Pkg. of 2. 12" × 12".

114300	Sticky Pages	$6.95

Stampin' Glitter

For the perfect amount of sparkle, try our different glitters. Apply with Heat & Stick powder, Tombow Multi-Purpose Adhesive, or a 2-Way Glue Pen, sold separately.

102023	Dazzling Diamonds (1/2 oz.)		$4.50
108797	Chunky Essentials (1 oz. ea.)	Red, White, Silver, Black	$15.95
111343	Chunky Sprinkles (1 oz. ea.)	Light Pink, Light Blue, Celery, Crystal Iris	$15.95
108796	Fine Cosmo (1/4 oz. ea.)	Rose Pink, Orchid, Light Blue, Celery, Turquoise	$13.95
114286	Fine Galaxy (1/4 oz. ea.)	Black, Silver, Red, Gold, Champagne	$13.95
114287	Fine Supernova (1/4 oz. ea.)	Chocolate, Olive, Orange, Pink, Aqua	$13.95

Micro Beads

Try using Tombow Multi-Purpose Adhesive, Sticky Strip, or Sticky Cuts to adhere these fun beads!

104266	Micro Beads	$5.25

Heat & Stick Powder

Use this product to apply Stampin' Glitter to your stamped image with precision. Acid free. 1/2 oz.

100625	Heat & Stick Powder	$4.50

stampin' kids® & die cuts

Stampin' Up! isn't just about fun for adults. Kids can enjoy crafting and playing
with tattoos and die-cut shapes made just for them.

Try these Build-a-Fairytale die cuts as paper dolls—a terrific way for your kids to imagine their own fairytale!

You can't always keep your kids from drawing on themselves, but you can provide a safe, fun way for them to stamp and draw on their skin without lasting consequences.

105668   Tattoo Kit I* $13.95
Navy pad, 6 markers (Black, Blue, Green, Henna, Red, Yellow)

105669   Tattoo Kit II* $13.95
Black pad, 6 markers (Blue, Green, Orange, Pink, Purple, Red)

Build-a-Fairytale

Build your own fairytale with die-cut shapes of princesses, carriages, and other things you need to build your own happily ever after. Create cards and scrapbook pages or laminate the images for children's playtime. Four 12" x 12" sheets; 1 of ea. design.

113950   Build-a-Fairytale $8.95
Chocolate Chip, Ruby Red, Pretty in Pink, So Saffron, Mellow Moss, Old Olive, Taken with Teal

Die Cuts

Whether you create a scene with our Build-a-Fairytale set or make multicolor die-cut blooms, our die cuts give you what you need. Mix and match the pieces until you've got them just right. Four 12" x 12" sheets; 1 of ea. color.

111376   Blooms $8.95
Real Red, Old Olive, Pumpkin Pie, Bashful Blue

112010   Blooms Again $8.95
Baja Breeze, Very Vanilla, Close to Cocoa, Kiwi Kiss

on board

Our versatile On Board products range from alphabets and accents to clipboards and albums. This high-quality, acid-free chipboard is designed to coordinate with many of our stamp sets and accessories. Color with our Craft Stampin' Pads, or decorate with stamped images, Designer Series paper, Hodgepodge Hardware, and more.

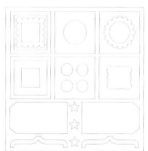

On Board Essentials

Essential pieces highlight cards, scrapbook pages, and other crafting projects. Assortment includes three 12" × 12" sheets: 1 ea. of 3 designs. More than 150 images included.

112085	Essentials	$12.95

On Board Loads of Letters

Multiple letters in three font styles make it easy to create words. Assortment includes three 12" × 12" sheets: 1 ea. of 3 designs.

112084	Loads of Letters	$12.95

On Board So Tweet
Assortment includes six 9" × 9" sheets. More than 80 images included.

113893	So Tweet	**$14.95**

On Board Batch of Blooms
Assortment includes six 9" × 9" sheets: 1 ea. of 6 designs with more than 200 images included.

112087	Batch of Blooms	**$14.95**

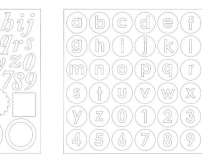

On Board Journals
Art Journal includes 50 sheets of unlined, acid-free paper. Approx. journal dimensions: 5-3/4" × 8-3/4". 5" × 5" Art Journal includes 20 sheets of Very Vanilla card stock. Approx. cover dimensions: 5-1/4 × 5-1/4".

107065	Art Journal	**$9.50**
108495	5" × 5" Art Journal	**$6.95**

On Board Clipboards
Customize with Designer Series paper to create seasonal photo holders, wish lists, or reminders. Sized exclusively for Stampin' Up!

109192	13" × 7-1/2"	**$15.95**
109191	4-1/2" × 9"	**$6.50**

On Board Book Basics
Use our thick chipboard to create personalized albums. Bind the covers with book clips, ribbon, or anything your heart desires! Long Board is sized and designed to use with the Sizzix Big Shot (page 193). Small: 5" × 7-1/2"; Large: 9-3/8" × 9-3/8"; Long: 5-3/4" × 13-3/4".

110713	Book Basics Large (9-3/8" × 9-3/8")	**$7.95**
110712	Book Basics Small (5" × 7-1/2")	**$5.95**
114320	Long Board (5-3/4" × 13-3/4")	**$6.95**

On Board Album
Larger 3-ring, chipboard album includes 10 8-1/2" × 8-1/2" page protectors. Cover size: 9-1/2" × 11-1/4".

112456	8-1/2" × 8-1/2" Ring Album	**$13.95**
112455	8-1/2" × 8-1/2" Page Protectors (10)	**$5.95**

On Board Timeless Type
Pieces include uppercase and lowercase alphabet as well as numbers. Multiple letters make it easy to create words. Assortment includes three 12" × 12" sheets: 1 ea. of 3 designs.

112083	Timeless Type	**$12.95**

On Board Lots of Letters
Assortment includes three 12" × 12" sheets with almost 200 letters, numbers, and accents.

109182	Lots of Letters	**$12.95**

1

Handheld Punches

1.	101227	1/16" Circle	$8.95

Punches

2.	104401	1-3/8" Circle	$15.95
3.	104403	1-1/4" Circle	$15.95
4.	109046	1" Circle	$10.95
5.	107217	3/4" Circle	$10.95
6.	104390	1/2" Circle	$5.95
7.	104388	Slit	$5.95
8.	109042	Photo Corners	$15.95
9.	112004	1-3/4" Circle	$15.95
10.	107304	Small Oval	$15.95
11.	107305	Large Oval	$15.95
12.	112082	Wide Oval	$15.95
13.	105090	Word Window	$15.95
14.	107272	Key Tag	$15.95
15.	105088	Double Rectangle	$5.95
16.	108341	Spiral	$10.95
17.	105089	Horizontal Slot	$5.95
18.	104400	1-1/4" Square	$15.95
19.	103375	1-3/8" Square	$15.95
20.	107215	Tag Corner	$6.95
21.	107214	Ticket Corner	$6.95
22.	109047	3/16" Corner Rounder	$6.95
23.	105934	Tag	$15.95
24.	108264	Small Tag	$15.95
25.	110710	Large Star	$15.95
26.	109045	Star	$10.95
27.	109041	5-Petal Flower	$15.95
28.	113694	Heart to Heart	$15.95
29.	107590	Designer Label	$15.95
30.	112091	Scallop Edge	$15.95
31.	113692	Eyelet Border	$15.95
32.	110711	Boho Blossoms	$15.95
33.	113693	Full Heart	$15.95
34.	109183	Trio Flower	$15.95
35.	110709	My Way	$15.95
36.	108340	Round Tab	$15.95
37.	109044	Snow Blossom	$10.95
38.	109043	Scallop Circle	$15.95
39.	112081	Scallop Square	$15.95

*Our punches are designed to work
with many of our stamp sets.
Use the punches and sets together
to create coordinating projects.*

PUNCH ARTWORK

Curly Label Punch Bundle

Make quick accents, journaling, or tags for any scrapbook page or card. This bundle includes the exclusive Cute & Curly stamp set and its coordinating Curly Label punch. Use them together to create small tags, focal points, or labels for your projects.

| 112966 | Curly Label Punch Bundle | $33.95 |

CUTE & CURLY STAMP ARTWORK (SET OF 4)

embossing

Embossing allows you to create beautiful raised images. For heat embossing, use our Heat Tool and Stampin' Emboss powder. Or try dry embossing with our Classy Brass® templates.

Classy Brass Templates

All Classy Brass templates feature exclusive designs that coordinate with popular Stampin' Up! sets. Most templates also include convenient guides for paper piercing.

109539	Punches Plus Coordinates with punches (page 184).	$20.95
107412	Seeing Spots Coordinates with Seeing Spots (page 108).	$9.95
109542	Pick a Petal Coordinates with Pick a Petal (page 114).	$21.95
111807	Floral Frenzy Coordinates with Eastern Blooms (page 94).	$15.95
109541	Priceless Coordinates with Priceless (page 121).	$15.95
109540	Dots	$15.95

PUNCHES PLUS   SEEING SPOTS   PICK A PETAL

FLORAL FRENZY   PRICELESS   DOTS

Stampin' Emboss Powder

Our embossing powder meets all of your embossing needs. Try embossing several layers to achieve a thick, dimensional look. 1/2 oz.

■	109133	Black	$4.75
	109132	White	$4.75
	109129	Gold	$4.75
	109131	Silver	$4.75
	109130	Clear	$4.75
	101930	Iridescent Ice	$4.75
	100477	Glassy Glaze Enamel (1 oz.)	$4.75

Heat & Stick Powder

Use this product to apply Stampin' Glitter to your stamped image with precision. Acid free. 1/2 oz.

100625	Heat & Stick Powder	$4.50

Embossing Buddy

Rub across paper to reduce static. Use before embossing or applying glitter.

103083	Embossing Buddy®	$5.95

Powder Pals

Keep your work area neat and save glitters and powders with these terrific tools. Comes with 2 trays and a brush for clean up.

102197	Powder Pals®	$19.95

Light Table

Our light table features a stainless steel frame, thick plexiglass top, tilt-up device, and bright, even light. This gives you the perfect surface for use with our Classy Brass templates. 10" × 12" work area.

102888	Light Table	$49.95

Stylus

Use small tip for lightweight papers and large tip for card stock.

100663	Stylus	$2.50

Empressor Stylus

Dual-tipped, roller-ball embossing tool features comfort grips and works with any template. Smooth-rolling action reduces paper tearing. Small tip is perfect for small patterns and lightweight papers; large tip works great on card stock.

100716	Empressor® Stylus	$10.95

Heat Tool

Use this electric heat tool with embossing powders, Heat & Stick Powder, and to heat-set pigment ink.

100005	Heat Tool	$29.95

albums

Use our premium, post-bound albums to store your scrapbook pages. The fabric has been pretreated with a stain-resistant coating. Includes 10 page protectors.

albums*	linen post albums *sm*			linen ring albums *sm*		
	12" × 12" $29.95	8-1/2" × 11" $24.95	6" × 6" $19.95	12" × 12" $26.95	8-1/2" × 11" $21.95	6" × 6" $16.95
NATURAL	104519	104520	104515	104511	104510	104509
MELLOW MOSS	105386	–	–	105393	–	105391
REAL RED	105383	–	–	105389	–	105387
NAVY	104518	–	–	104514	–	104512
page protectors**	$10.95	$7.95	$6.95	$10.95	$7.95	$6.95
CLEAR	100670	103145	103687	104522	104523	104521

storage

COLOR CADDY EXTENDER KIT

Color Caddy

Holds 48 Classic or Craft pads and 48 refills. Rotates for easy access. Some assembly required. Pads and refills not included. The Color Caddy extender kit includes 3 stacking trays to accommodate 12 additional Stampin' Up! pads. Extender rod and assembly instructions included.

104335	Color Caddy®	$59.95
107063	Color Caddy Extender Kit	$14.95

STAMPIN' STORE CONTAINERS (6)

Stampin' Stack & Store

The Stack & Store Caddy is exclusively designed to be used with our Stampin' Store containers. Stack & Store Caddy is housed on a turntable, and the containers are easily removed with one hand! Caddy holds 24 containers or 48 mini containers.

109127	Stack & Store Caddy	$34.95
103649	Stampin' Store Containers (2-1/2" × 7/8")	$3.95

Ribbon Keepers

Our exclusive stackable storage boxes offer an organized way to store your ribbon. Create customized ribbon storage based on your needs. Each package includes 2 boxes, 2 divider slides, 6 connector tabs, 12 rubber feet, and instructions for assembly. The small keeper holds 3/8" ribbon. The medium keeper holds 5/8", 7/8", 1", and 1-1/4" ribbon. The large keeper holds 1/4" ribbon.

107634	Small (2)	$11.95
107635	Medium (2)	$15.95
107636	Large (2)	$18.95

Forget-Me-Not Keeper

Use for photo storage or card organization. Includes 12 dividers that allow you to sort photos by theme, or cards by month or occasion. 8-5/8" × 6-5/8" × 5".

105525	Forget-Me-Not Keeper®	$11.95

Stampin' Color Index Labels

Includes labels for the 2008–2009 In Colors. Place on the ends of your ink pads or use them to catalog or file your card stock. 66 labels per sheet; sheet size 5" × 6".

113034	Color Index Labels (2)	$3.95

Craft Keepers

Safe storage for photos, papers, card stock, templates, and more. Velcro® closure. Expands to 1" thick. 3 per pkg.

104182	8-1/2" × 11" (actual size: 9" × 11-1/2")	$6.95
104181	12" × 12" (actual size: 13-1/2" × 13-1/2")	$7.95

Paper Holders and Dividers

Our vertical paper holders make it easy to store and protect paper while keeping it visible and within reach. Paper holders store up to 200 sheets of card stock. Use the paper holder dividers (sold separately) to separate paper by color or pattern.

105527	Paper Holder 8-1/2" × 11"	$6.95
105526	Dividers 8-1/2" × 11" (4)	$5.25
105528	Paper Holder 12" × 12"	$7.95
105529	Dividers 12" × 12" (4)	$5.95

tools

The key to completing any project is having the right set of tools. On these two pages, you'll find tools to help with cutting, tearing, measuring, folding, and more. Whether you want to align an image perfectly, create a row of paper-pierced holes, or set eyelets in a snap, Stampin' Up! has what you need.

Glass Mat

Mat provides a smooth glass cutting surface that allows a cutting blade to glide without dragging or skipping. Use with the Circle Scissor Plus. 13" × 13".

112531	Glass Mat	$19.95

Cutting Mat

This no-slip mat allows for safe cutting while protecting your work surface. Grid lines provide a guide for precise cutting with your hobby blade or craft knife. 12" × 18".

101087	Cutting Mat	$15.95

Grid Paper

Oversized pad of paper protects your stamping work surfaces. Serves as scratch paper and makes cleanup a snap! Features include a standard card-dimension list and space for writing a wish list.

102787	Grid Paper (100 sheets)	$9.95

Mat Pack

Paper-piercing pad, paper-piercing template, and setting mat, each 4" × 4".

105826	Mat Pack	$9.95

Circle Scissor Plus

Making perfect circles has never been simpler! Use the Circle Scissor Plus to cut and draw circles with ease. Works best with the Glass Mat. Replacement blades are sold separately in a package of 3.

112530	Circle Scissor Plus	$29.95
112532	Replacement Blades	$3.95

Coluzzle Cutting System

Includes circle and oval template, cutting mat, and cutting knife all packaged in our 8-1/2" × 11" Craft Keeper.

102264	Coluzzle® Starter Set	$19.95
102721	Coluzzle Refill Blades (2)	$4.50

Crafters' Tool Kit

Includes 3/16" and 1/8" anywhere hole punches, universal eyelet setter, two needles, paper-piercing tool, bottle-nosed pliers with wire cutter, cross-lock tweezers, and hammer. Also includes paper-piercing pad, paper-piercing template, and setting mat, each 4" × 4". All packaged in a durable nylon zip case with outside pocket. Instructions included.

104310	Crafters' Tool Kit	$39.95

Tabletop Paper Cutter

Precise paper cutter features stainless-steel precision-ground blades and is ideal for cardmaking and scrapbooking.

| 106959 | Tabletop Paper Cutter | $45.95 |

Stamp-a-ma-jig

Use this stamp positioner for precise stamp alignment every time. Nonskid base. Includes reusable, wipe-clean imaging sheet for easy placement.

| 101049 | Stamp-a-ma-jig® | $11.95 |

Paper Cutter

Portable and lightweight. Cuts paper up to 12". Features easy-to-read grid lines and black base. Measures widths up to 15-1/2". Comes with 2 cutting blades. Refills include either a cutting and scoring blade or 2 cutting blades.

104152	Paper Cutter	$24.95
104154	Cutting & Scoring Blade Refills	$5.95
104153	Cutting Blade Refills	$5.95

Stampin' Scrub

Dual-sided tray contains replaceable black fiber scrubbing pads. Clean stamp on one side, blot dry on the other. Sized to fit even our largest stamps. Each pad is approx. 7" × 5-3/4".

| 102642 | Stampin' Scrub | $16.95 |
| 101230 | Stampin' Scrub Refill Pads (2) | $9.95 |

Hobby Blade

Extra sharp, with 5 refill blades. Comes in a convenient storage tube.

| 102449 | Hobby Blade & Refills | $4.50 |

Stampin' Mist Stamp Cleaner

Lightly scented spray cleans and conditions your rubber stamps. For best results, clean stamp immediately after use.

| 102394 | Stampin' Mist (2 oz.) | $4.50 |
| 101022 | Stampin' Mist Refill (8 oz.) | $9.50 |

Cutter Kit

Use this convenient and portable cutter kit for all of your projects on the go! Includes rotary cutter, perforating tool, scoring tool, and a 7-sided distressing tool.

| 106958 | Cutter Kit | $16.95 |

Crop-A-Dile

Circle punch through chipboard, tin, and multiple paper layers with ease. Its built-in 1/8" and 3/16" eyelet setters silently and easily set eyelets of both sizes.

| 108362 | Crop-A-Dile™ | $29.95 |

Craft & Rubber Scissors

These sharp, short-bladed scissors are especially suited for trimming your rubber stamps before assembling them. 1-3/4" blade length.

| 103179 | Craft & Rubber Scissors | $19.95 |

Bone Folder

Use to score paper and make crisp folds.

| 102300 | Bone Folder | $6.95 |

Paper Snips

These small, thin-bladed scissors provide expert cutting in even the tiniest of areas, and the precision-ground tips allow you to cut to the end of the blade. 2-1/2" blade length.

| 103579 | Paper Snips | $9.95 |

Sanding Blocks

Use to distress the surface of your paper or to sand a rough edge.

| 103301 | Sanding Blocks (2) | $3.50 |

The Tearing Edge

Create natural-looking torn edges with precision. Approx. 13" × 1-1/2".

| 102930 | The Tearing Edge | $19.95 |

Craft & Paper Scissors

High-quality crafting scissors cut ribbon easily and create a smooth, clean cut. 3-3/4" blade length.

| 108360 | Craft & Paper Scissors | $29.95 |

Crimper

Crimps card stock and paper up to 6-1/2" wide.

| 101618 | Crimper | $19.95 |

189

coloring tools

Encore!® Pads

Add a rich, metallic look to your stamped projects with these acid-free, fade-resistant pigment ink pads. Metallic inks should be heat set when used in a scrapbook. These inks come in stackable, easy-to-hold pads. *sm*

	101017	Gold Pad	$8.95
	101242	Gold Refill (1/2 oz.)	$4.25
	101039	Silver Pad	$8.95
	102124	Silver Refill (1/2 oz.)	$4.25

VersaMark

Create a tone-on-tone or a watermark effect with this pad and marker. Acid free. *sm*

102283	VersaMark Pad	$7.50
102193	VersaMark Pad Refill (1/2 oz.)	$3.95
100901	VersaMarker	$3.25

Pencil Sharpener

Sharp steel blade creates a fine point with 2 sizes that accommodate Stampin' Up! Watercolor pencils and crayons. Removable receptacle for shavings keeps things neat.

100745	Pencil Sharpener	$4.95

StāzOn Ink Pads

This quick-drying, permanent ink works great on nonporous surfaces.

	101406	Jet Black Pad	$7.95
	102566	Jet Black Refill (1/2 oz.)	$4.95
	106960	White Pad & Refill (1/2 oz.)	$11.95
	106961	White Refill (1/2 oz.)	$4.95

StāzOn Cleaner

StāzOn stamp cleaner is especially formulated to clean and condition stamps after use with StāzOn ink. This cleaner is used to prevent staining that can occur when using solvent-based inks.

109196	Cleaner (2 oz.)	$4.95

Stampin' Write Journalers

Fade-resistant, waterproof, pigment markers ideal for journaling and scrapbooking. Tip sizes: .6mm and 2.3 mm bullet. *sm*

	105394	Basic Black	$3.25
	109123	Basic Brown	$3.25

uni-ball® Signo Gel Pen

The smooth-rolling ink of this gel pen allows you to add text or creative touches on dark card stock. Medium ballpoint tip. *sm*

105021	White	$3.95

applicators

Color Spritzer Tool

Achieve spectacular effects using a Stampin' Write marker with this convenient tool. The tool mists the ink from the marker to create a spattered look. Marker not included.

107066	Color Spritzer Tool	$12.95

Stamping Sponges

101610	Stamping Sponges (3)	$3.50

Sponge Daubers

102892	Sponge Daubers (12)	$10.95

Stipple Brushes

No. 2 and No. 4. 2 per pkg.

101399	Stipple Brushes	$6.95

Brayer

Use for special-effect backgrounds and uniform inking on large stamps. Includes handle and soft rubber attachment.

102395	Handle with Rubber Attachment	$12.50

Blender Pens

2 brush tips on each. Use with Watercolor pencils, Watercolor Wonder Crayons, Classic Stampin' Pads, ink refills, and Stampin' Pastels to blend color. Acid free and xylene free. 3 per pkg.

102845	Blender Pens (3)	$9.95

Aqua Painter

Use this versatile tool for controlled water coloring. It's less messy and more transportable than a cup and watercolor brush. To use, fill reservoir with water. (1 medium and 1 large per pkg.)

103954	Aqua Painter	$16.95

adhesives

Dotto

Tiny repositionable adhesive dots in a convenient dispenser. Acid free. .585". *sm*

103305	Dotto®	$12.95
100902	Dotto Refill	$6.50

Sticky Strip

Use this double-sided, extra-tacky strip to adhere micro beads or ribbon and make three-dimensional items stick tightly. Acid free. Approx. 1/4" wide, approx. 10 yds.

104294	Sticky Strip	$6.95

Crystal Effects

Add a dimensional, lacquered look to any stamped image. Acid free. 2 oz.

101055	Crystal Effects®	$6.25

Adhesive Remover

This adhesive remover works like an eraser. Note: It does not remove tape. 2" x 2"

103684	Adhesive Remover	$3.50

Tombow Multi Purpose Adhesive

This adhesive is temporary when allowed to momentarily dry before adhering or permanent when adhered promptly. Use it with beads and glitter or to secure Designer Series paper to chipboard. Acid free. .875 oz.

110755	Tombow® Adhesive	$3.95

2-Way Glue Pen

This adhesive is temporary when allowed to dry before adhering or permanent when adhered promptly. Use to adhere glitter. Acid free. 10 grams.

100425	2-Way Glue Pen	$3.50

SNAIL Adhesive

Double-sided, permamnent adhesive dispensed continuously. Acid free. .472".

104332	SNAIL Adhesive	$6.95
104331	SNAIL Refill	$4.50

Anywhere Glue Stick

Rectangle shape allows you access to even the corners of your project. Acid Free. 20 grams each.

104045	Anywhere Glue Stick (2)	$3.95

Stampin' Dimensionals

1/16" thick double-sided, adhesive foam dots. Acid free.

104430	Stampin' Dimensionals (300)	$3.95

Glue Dots

Glue Dots are a super-sticky adhesive designed for use on three-dimensional accents. No fumes, no mess, no drying time required. Acid free.

103683	Mini Glue Dots Approx 3/16" dia., 300 dots.	$4.95
104183	Pop-Up Glue Dots Approx 1/2" dia., 1/8" thick, 75 dots.	$3.95

stampin' around

Look for this symbol marking our Stampin' Around wheels throughout the catalog. Ink cartridges are sold on pages 153–155.

Stampin' Around Wheel Storage

Each standard container stores 10 wheels; jumbo container stores 6 wheels.

105743	Standard (2)	$6.95
105741	Jumbo (2)	$6.95

Stampin' Around Handles

Does not include cartridge or wheel. Ink cartridges are sold on pages 153–155.

102971	Stampin' Around Handle	$3.95
103661	Stampin' Around Jumbo Handle	$5.95

Stampin' Around Wheel Guide

Wheel perfect background papers, borders, or mitered corners without worrying about crooked lines or overlapping images with this handy tool. Rubber feet keep the guide from moving or slipping. The guide can be configured for both standard and jumbo wheels.

104834	Wheel Guide	$9.95

Uninked Cartridges

These cartridges come uninked, ready to create your own cartridge with any of our Classic ink refills.

101529	Cartridge	$5.25
103678	Jumbo Cartridge	$7.50

décor elements

Decorate your walls and create custom décor with our easy-to-apply vinyl elements. Use them to redecorate an entire room or to refresh select pieces such as frames and tiles. For video instructions about application and removal and to view our full line of Décor Elements products, contact your demonstrator or visit www.stampinup.com/decorelements.

Let our artwork enhance your surroundings. With our vinyl Décor Elements, you have a variety of options for giving your home a new look without the high price of repainting and redecorating. Since we offer coordinating stamp sets, you can create home décor pieces to match.

CHOCOLATE	KRAFT	WHITE		
114878	114875	114881	Filigree *(medium)*	$29.95
114877	114874	114880	Filigree *(small)*	$24.95
114115	114077	—	Manhattan Flower	$23.95

CERTAINLY CELERY	CHOCOLATE	WHITE		
114783	114780	114777	Always Bird *(medium)*	$15.95
114782	114779	114776	Always Bird *(small)*	$9.95
—	114136	114135	Flourishes	$14.95
	114142	114141	Family *(medium)*	$21.95
—	114118	114080	Family *(small)*	$16.95
	114892	115163	Familia *(medium)*	$21.95
—	114891	115162	Familia *(small)*	$16.95

CHOCOLATE	BASHFUL BLUE	PRETTY IN PINK		
114706	114703	114700	Nursery Necessities *(large)*	$29.95
114705	114702	114699	Nursery Necessities *(medium)*	$19.95
114704	114701	114698	Nursery Necessities Border	$12.95

Décor Elements Applicator

Apply Décor Elements designs with this convenient angled plastic applicator. Handy for both applying & removing. Approx 2-7/8" x 2-1/4".

114285	Applicator	$1.95

Decor Elements Sheets

Each package includes with two (2) 12" x 24" sheets of vinyl in specified color, along with two (2) 12" x 24" sheets of transfer tape to make using your vinyl pieces easy. Instructions for use are included.

	114336	Kraft	$12.95
	114337	Chocolate	$12.95
	114335	White	$12.95
	114334	Dark Gray	$12.95

FILIGREE
MEDIUM:
SMALL:

MANHATTAN FLOWER

ALWAYS BIRD
MEDIUM:
SMALL:

FLOURISHES

FAMILY
MEDIUM:
SMALL:

family

FAMILIA
MEDIUM:
SMALL:

familia

NURSERY NECESSITIES
LARGE:
MEDIUM:
BORDER:

ALL DIMENSIONS (W x H) ARE APPROXIMATE AND ARE TAKEN FROM THE LARGEST LETTER OR IMAGE IN THE SET UNLESS NOTED OTHERWISE.

Sizzix Big Shot

Stampin' Up! is pleased to team up with Sizzix to offer you a multipurpose die-cutting system! With the Sizzix Big Shot Starter Kit and dies from Stampin' Up!, you can create die-cut shapes, envelopes, and tags with ease! The Big Shot works with card stock, Designer Series paper, fabric, chipboard, plastic, and more. With this machine, your projects will come together in seconds!

Kit Contents

Big Shot Die-Cut Machine
Multipurpose Platform and Standard Cutting Pads
2 Stampin' Up! Exclusive Bigz Dies (Scallop Envelope and Top Note)
1 Stampin' Up! Exclusive Sizzlits 4-Pack (Birds & Blooms)
1 Stampin' Up! Exclusive Decorative Strip (Decorative Strip Billboard)
Decorative Strip Cutting Pads and Extended Spacer Platform

Big Shot Starter Kit
To get started, you need the Big Shot die-cut machine, Standard Cutting Pad, Multipurpose Platform (both included with the Big Shot) and a die.

| 116314 | Big Shot Starter Kit | $195.95 |
| 116315 | Big Shot Starter Kit with Bag | $259.95 |

Texturz Impressions Pad
Use with Silicone Rubber, Texturz Texture Plates, and Multipurpose Platform to provide soft, detailed backgrounds.

| 114614 | Texturz Impressions Pad | $5.95 |

Texturz Silicone Rubber
Use with Impressions Pad, Texturz Texture Plates, and Multipurpose Platform to provide soft, detailed backgrounds.

| 114615 | Texturz Silicone Rubber | $5.95 |

Decorative Strip Cutting Pads
Along with the Extended Spacer Platform (sold separately), these pads accommodate the extra-long format of Decorative Strip dies. Includes 1 pair, 13" long.

| 113479 | Decorative Strip Cutting Pads | $7.95 |

Big Shot Die-Cut Machine
With the Big Shot, you can create die cuts with any of our exclusive Stampin' Up! dies— or any Sizzix die. Machine includes standard cutting pads and multipurpose platform so you can start cutting immediately.

| 113439 | Big Shot Die-Cut Machine | $99.95 |

Standard Cutting Pads
Essential for cutting with the Bigz, Originals, and Sizzlits dies, the replacement cutting pads can be flipped over for twice the wear. Includes 1 pair.

| 113475 | Standard Cutting Pads | $8.95 |

Doctor's Bag
This bag features Stampin' Up!'s logo and is sized to hold the Big Shot die-cut machine, cutting pad, and dies for convenient storage and transport.

| 113474 | Doctor's Bag | $69.95 |

Extended Cutting Pads
Essential for cutting with the Bigz XL dies, the cutting pads can be flipped over for twice the wear. Includes 1 pair.

| 113478 | Extended Cutting Pads | $19.95 |

Extended Spacer Platform
Along with Decorative Strip cutting pads (sold separately), the Extended Spacer Platform is required to use Decorative Strip dies in the Big Shot die-cut machine.

| 113477 | Extended Spacer Platform | $9.95 |

Premium Crease Pad
Use this pad in the Big Shot die-cut machine to create subtle fold lines for Bigz and Originals cards, envelopes, bags, boxes and pockets.

| 113476 | Extended Spacer Platform | $8.95 |

bigz xl dies

The Bigz XL dies are rule-based dies measuring 6" x 13-3/4" that cut through various materials such as paper, plastic, and corkboard. These dies also work with our chipboard (page 183) when your project needs a sturdy backing or base. Use Bigz XL dies with Extended Cutting Pads to create boxes, bags, pennants, envelopes, and more!

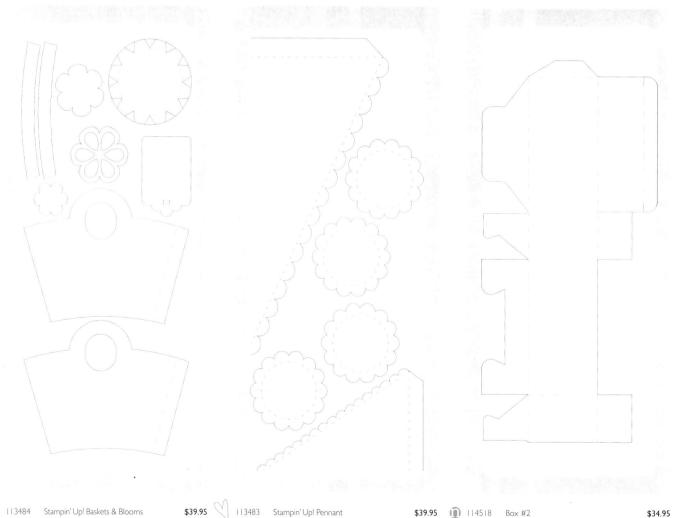

♡	113484	Stampin' Up! Baskets & Blooms	$39.95	♡	113483	Stampin' Up! Pennant	$39.95

114518   Box #2 $34.95

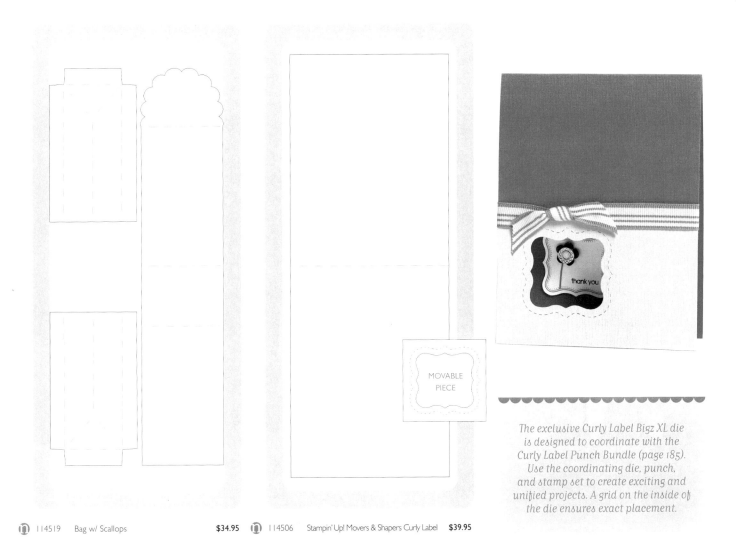

MOVABLE
PIECE

The exclusive Curly Label Bigz XL die is designed to coordinate with the Curly Label Punch Bundle (page 185). Use the coordinating die, punch, and stamp set to create exciting and unified projects. A grid on the inside of the die ensures exact placement.

114519   Bag w/ Scallops   **$34.95**   114506   Stampin' Up! Movers & Shapers Curly Label   **$39.95**

bigz clear dies

The Bigz dies are rule-based dies measuring 5-1/2" x 6" that cut through various materials such as paper, plastic, and chipboard. Use them with Standard Cutting Pads. Clear-based dies offer easy positioning—you can see exactly what you're cutting—which allows even more personalization on your project.

114532   Card, Telephone & Address   **$19.95**   114533   Clear Circle   **$19.95**   114534   Flower   **$19.95**

bigz dies

The Bigz dies are rule-based dies measuring 5-1/2" × 6" that cut through various materials such as paper, plastic, and chipboard. Use them with Standard Cutting Pads to create ornaments, boxes, embellishments, tags, envelopes, and more.

The Serif Essentials Alphabet includes all letters of the alphabet on seven dies.

113464   Serif Essentials Alphabet (set of 7)   **$149.95**

113457   Stampin' Up! Tulipe   **$21.95**

113463   Stampin' Up! Top Note   **$21.95**

114520   Flower, Daisies #2   **$19.95**

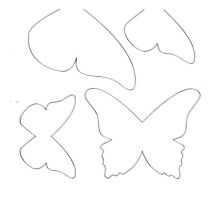

114507   Stampin' Up! Beautiful Butterflies   **$21.95**

113462   Stampin' Up! Scallop Envelope*   **$21.95**

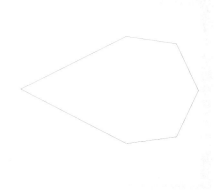

113473   5-Point 3D Star*   **$19.95**

114521　Frame, Oval Scallop　**$19.95**	113466　Pillow Box*　**$19.95**	113468　Scallop Circle　**$19.95**
113469　Scallop Circle #2　**$19.95**	113470　Flower Layers w/ Leaf　**$19.95**	114522　Decorative Accent #2　**$19.95**
113465　Bird w/ Leaves and Flower　**$19.95**	114523　Decorative Accents　**$19.95**	113467　Petal Card*　**$19.95**
113471　Build a Flower　**$19.95**	113472　Circle 3D Ornament*　**$19.95**	114524　Fringed Flower　**$19.95**

CUT ———— SCORE　PERFORATION · · · ·

197

sizzlits decorative strip dies

Sizzlits Decorative Strips measure 2-1/4" x 12". These chemically etched dies cut through card stock and Designer Series paper. Use them with Extended Spacer Platform and Decorative Strip Cutting Pads.

Ⓝ 114510	Stampin' Up! Billboard		$21.95
113452	Stampin' Up! Join in the Cheer		$21.95
113456	Swirly		$19.95
113455	Loopy Flowers		$19.95
113454	Flowers		$19.95

113453	Naturally Serif	$19.95
114529	Birds & Branches	$19.95

originals dies

The Originals™ dies are rule-based dies measuring 4-3/4" × 5-1/5" that cut through various materials such as paper, plastic, and chipboard. Use them with Standard Cutting Pads.

113458   Flower Layers $15.95

Create shapes in seconds with our Big Shot die-cut machine and dies. Use them as embellishments, as shown on the Enjoy treat. With our On Board Book Basics Long Board and Originals dies, you can create customized ornaments quickly.

113461   Stars #2 $15.95   114526   Circles #2 $15.95

113459   Leaves #2 $15.95   114525   Ovals $15.95   113460   Snowflake #2 $15.95   114527   Flower Layers #3 $15.95

sizzlits dies

Sizzlits dies measure 2-1/4" x 2-1/2". These chemically etched dies cut through single layers of card stock and Designer Series paper. Use them with Standard Cutting Pads and Multipurpose Platform.

114511	Stampin' Up! Little Leaves	$4.95	113444	Sparkle	$4.95	113450 Go Go Boots Alphabet Set (set of 12) $69.95
113440	Buttons #5	$4.95	113441	Swirls Scribbles	$4.95	113442 Daisy Flower $4.95
113445	Pumpkin Faces	$4.95	113443	Pumpkin #4	$4.95	114530 Flower Blossom $4.95

sizzlits 4-pack dies

Sizzlits dies (set of 4) measure 2-1/4" x 2-1/2". These chemically etched dies cut through card stock and Designer Series paper. Use them with Standard Cutting Pads and Multipurpose Platform.

Each of the dies on this page is a set of four, so you'll instantly have a variety of coordinating images. It's simple to create projects that are fun, versatile, and coordinating.

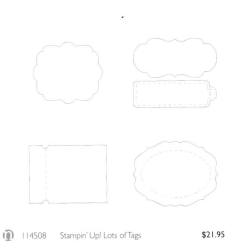

114508   Stampin' Up! Lots of Tags $21.95

113485   Stampin' Up! Birds & Blooms $21.95   114509   Stampin' Up! Big Bold Cupcakes $21.95   113447   Spring Flowers Set $19.95

113448   Hearts Set $19.95   113449   Snowflakes Set #2 $19.95   113446   Build a Flower Set #2 $19.95

embosslits dies

Embosslits dies measure 2-1/4" x 2-1/2". These chemically etched dies include a positive and negative image that allows simultaneous cutting and embossing. Embosslits cut through card stock and Designer Series paper. Use them with Standard Cutting Pads and the Multipurpose Platform.

:: sneak peek ::
Here's a sneak peek at our Manhattan Flower die—coming in March. Ask your demonstrator for details.

114516   Stampin' Up! Cherry Blossom $11.95   114515   Stampin' Up! Flower Burst $11.95

114513   Stampin' Up! Sweetest Stem $11.95   114514   Stampin' Up! Simple Flower $11.95

Textured Impressions Die

Designed to coordinate with our Fifth Avenue Floral set (page 106), the Manhattan Flower die creates an elegant, embossed card front image.

114517   Stampin' Up! $7.95
Manhattan Flower

114528   Flower $11.95

BIG SHOT DIES SHOWN AT 40%

texturz plates

Texturz plates create subtle patterns and designs on thin surfaces, giving your project the perfect embossed background. Set of 3 double-sided plates offer 6 unique and exciting options. Use with the Multipurpose Platform, Impressions Pad, and Silicone Rubber (sold separately).

114512   Stampin' Up! Backgrounds 1 $11.95

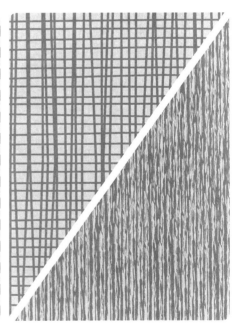

114531   Texture Plates Kit #4 $9.95

203

| 109689 | Batty* | $8.50 |

| 105957 | Bold Snowflakes* | $8.50 |

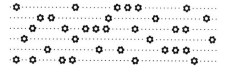

| 109686 | Christmas Chatter* | $8.50 |

| 111254 | Classic Stars (p. 66) | $8.50 |

| 111255 | Daisy Dash (p. 115) | $8.50 |

| 109684 | Doodle (p. 88) | $8.50 |

| 111256 | Dotted Lines (p. 120) | $8.50 |

| 114696 | Friendly Words (p. 81) | $8.50 |

| 111257 | Happy, Happy Birthday (p. 40) | $8.50 |

| 112480 | Haunting* | $8.50 |

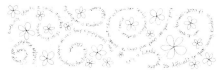

| 111201 | It's Beautiful (p. 94) | $8.50 |

| 106750 | Kindness (p. 52) | $8.50 |

| 109685 | Neighborhood (p. 77) | $8.50 |

| 111258 | Nursery Letters (p. 66) | $8.50 |

| 111259 | Pinch Me (p. 28) | $8.50 |

| 107213 | Scatter Sunshine (p. 52) | $8.50 |

| 109687 | See You Around (p. 48) | $8.50 |

| 109683 | So Swirly (p. 94) | $8.50 |

| 111260 | Something Fishy (p. 70) | $8.50 |

| 107559 | Spot On (p. 120) | $8.50 |

| 111262 | Stems & Silhouettes* | $8.50 |

| 113832 | Symphony (p. 116) | $8.50 |

| 109688 | Whimsy (p. 88) | $8.50 |

| 107560 | Watercolor Vine (p. 84) | $8.50 |

standard wheel index

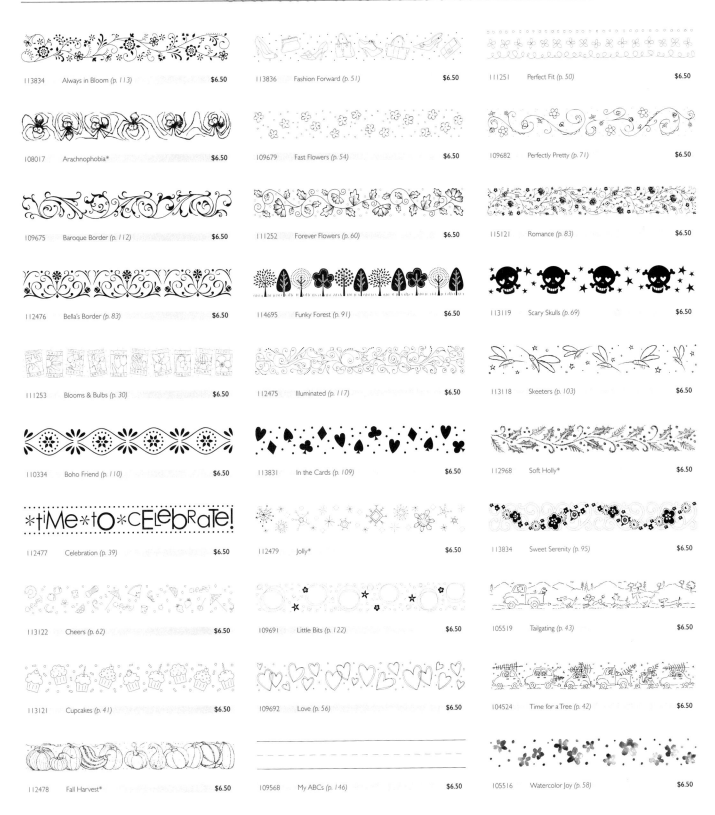

113834 Always in Bloom (p. 113) $6.50	113836 Fashion Forward (p. 51) $6.50	111251 Perfect Fit (p. 50) $6.50
108017 Arachnophobia* $6.50	109679 Fast Flowers (p. 54) $6.50	109682 Perfectly Pretty (p. 71) $6.50
109675 Baroque Border (p. 112) $6.50	111252 Forever Flowers (p. 60) $6.50	115121 Romance (p. 83) $6.50
112476 Bella's Border (p. 83) $6.50	114695 Funky Forest (p. 91) $6.50	113119 Scary Skulls (p. 69) $6.50
111253 Blooms & Bulbs (p. 30) $6.50	112475 Illuminated (p. 117) $6.50	113118 Skeeters (p. 103) $6.50
110334 Boho Friend (p. 110) $6.50	113831 In the Cards (p. 109) $6.50	112968 Soft Holly* $6.50
112477 Celebration (p. 39) $6.50	112479 Jolly* $6.50	113834 Sweet Serenity (p. 95) $6.50
113122 Cheers (p. 62) $6.50	109691 Little Bits (p. 122) $6.50	105519 Tailgating (p. 43) $6.50
113121 Cupcakes (p. 41) $6.50	109692 Love (p. 56) $6.50	104524 Time for a Tree (p. 42) $6.50
112478 Fall Harvest* $6.50	109568 My ABCs (p. 146) $6.50	105516 Watercolor Joy (p. 58) $6.50

stamp index

accessories index

Proprietary Rights in Trademarks and Copyrights

The contents of this catalog are protected by federal trademark and copyright registrations. Reproduction of the catalog or any portion thereof is strictly prohibited. Purchasers of Stampin' Up! products are authorized to sell hand-stamped artwork made with our copyrighted designs only in accordance with Stampin' Up!'s Angel Policy, a copy of which can be found on the Stampin' Up! Web site at www.stampinup.com, or obtained from a Stampin' Up! demonstrator. Permission is not granted to mechanically reproduce stamped images.

Ordering

All products in this catalog may be purchased only through a Stampin' Up! demonstrator. Demonstrators are independent contractors and are not employees of Stampin' Up! To help your demonstrator ensure accuracy in taking your order, always include item number, description, and price of each item ordered. Your demonstrator will provide you with two copies of your order. Please retain these copies for your personal records. You have a right to cancel order within 3 days of placing it. Ask your demonstrator for more details.

Delivery

We ship through the best carrier available. Product is usually shipped to deliver within 7 business days from the date the order is received by the company. Stampin' Up! shall not be liable for any delay in shipment that is caused in whole or in part by circumstances beyond Stampin' Up!'s control.

Guarantee

We guarantee products to be free from manufacturing defects for a period of 90 days after the shipping date. Missing items, incorrect shipments, and defective or damaged merchandise must be reported to your demonstrator within 90 days of the shipping date. This guarantee does not cover merchandise damaged through accident or misuse. If you should require assistance, please contact your demonstrator.

Exchanges & Refunds

New, unused merchandise may be exchanged at no charge within 90 days of the shipping date. The merchandise must be in the current catalog and in original shipping condition. Stamps that have been assembled cannot be exchanged. Sorry, we do not offer cash refunds. The customer is responsible for return shipping charges. If you should require assistance, please contact your demonstrator.

Limitations

Stampin' Up! reserves the right to issue a refund or substitute merchandise of similar quality and value for items that are discontinued or out of stock. The decision to discontinue merchandise and the choice of whether to issue a refund or substitution belongs solely to Stampin' Up! The items sold are craft items, and your results may vary from the examples shown. Also, actual stamps may vary somewhat in size from the images shown in this catalog, and this difference in size shall not be deemed a manufacturing defect. Information about properties of certain products (such as acid content, lignin content, and other properties affecting a product's performance or suitability for a particular use) is supplied by the product manufacturers and/or suppliers. Stampin' Up! relies on this information and does not conduct independent tests to verify the accuracy of the information supplied by product manufacturers and suppliers.

Trademark Ownership

Tombow is a registered trademark of American Tombow, Inc. Empressor is a trademark and Dotto and Stamp-a-ma-jig are registered trademarks of EK Success Ltd. Glue Dots is a registered trademark of Glue Dots International. uni-ball is a registered trademark of Mitsubishi Pencil Company, Ltd. Coluzzle is a registered trademark of Provo Craft & Novelty. Watercolor Wonder is a trademark and Aqua Painter, Bold Brights, Classy Brass, Color Caddy, Color Coach, Crystal Effects, Definitely Decorative, Earth Elements, Embossing Buddy, Forget-Me-Not Keeper, Hodgepodge Hardware, In Color, Powder Pals, Rich Regals, Simply Scrappin', Simply Sent, SNAIL Adhesive, Soft Subtles, Stampin' Around, Stampin' Dimensionals, Stampin' Emboss, Stampin' Glitter, Stampin' Ink, Stampin' Kids, Stampin' Memories and the Stampin' Memories logo, Stampin' Mist, Stampin' Pad, Stampin' Pastels, Stampin' Scrub, Stampin' Up! and the Stampin' Up! box logo, Stampin' Write, Two-Step Stampin' and the 2-Step Stampin' design, The Tearing Edge, and Write Me a Memory are registered trademarks of Stampin' Up!, Inc. VersaMarker is a trademark and Encore, StazOn, and VersaMark are registered trademarks of Tsukineko, LLC. Crop-A-Dile is a trademark of We R Memory Keepers.

Stampin' Up!
12907 South 3600 West
Riverton, UT 84065
www.stampinup.com

Want to try stamping? These convenient and cost-effective options are a terrific way to start!
Try a kit or one of the individual stamps shown below. The stamp can be used over and over again to
create cards, notepads—anything you can imagine. Pick your favorite and see how easy it is.

{Just had to write to say}

thank you

a little note of thanks

{Just had to write to say}

thank you

Mini Note Kit

This kit offers two terrific images you can use to convey your thanks. Kit
includes a double-mounted stamp, 4 Whisper White Gift Notes & Envelopes,
and a Chocolate Chip Classic Stampin' Spot.

116209	Note of Thanks	$9.95

happy birthday

THE SECRET OF HAPPINESS IS
TO COUNT YOUR BLESSINGS,
NOT YOUR BIRTHDAYS.

THE SECRET OF HAPPINESS IS
TO COUNT YOUR BLESSINGS,
NOT YOUR BIRTHDAYS.

happy birthday

Mini Note Kit

No one will be able to resist this heartfelt birthday message. Kit includes
a double-mounted stamp, 4 Whisper White Gift Notes & Envelopes, and a
Chocolate Chip Classic Stampin' Spot.

116210	Birthdays Count	$9.95

together FOREVER

set of 1 | **Forever**
114494 $5.95

beautiful little baby

set of 1 | **Beautiful Baby**
114492 $7.95

Happy Birthday to you!

set of 1 | **Birthday Wish**
114486 $6.95

SO GLAD
YOU ARE ONE
of my dearest friends

set of 1 | **Glad Friends**
114490 $5.95

set of 1 | **Flowers in Silhouette**
114498 $7.95

CELEBRATE
CELEBRATE party dream WISH
CELEBRATE laugh
HOORAY party HAPPY DAY party
celebrate
CONGRATS • CONGRATS • CONGRATS

set of 1 | **Celebrations**
114496 $7.95

THANK YOU

set of 1 | **Elegant Thank You**
114484 $6.95
ESP 114552 Gracias

set of 1 | **Fun Flowers**
114488 $5.95